Author: Chris Wardle

Ginn
Halley Court, Jordan Hill, Oxford OX2 8EJ
a division of Harcourt Education Limited

www.myprimary.co.uk
Help and support for teachers plus the widest range of education solutions

Ginn is a registered trademark of Harcourt Education Limited

© Harcourt Education Limited 2005

This book is copyright and reproduction of the whole or part without the publishers' written permission is prohibited.

Key Grammar Workbook Starter Level
ISBN: 978 0602 20679 6
Starter Level Easy Order Pack: 978 0602 20621 5
Starter Level Workbook 6 Pack: 978 0602 20643 7

First published 2005

20 19 18 17 16
15 14

Cover illustration by Pet Gotohda
Cover design by Tom Cole
Designed by Nicki Wise, Te Marama Design
Illustrations by Andrea Pretrlik Huseinovic, Maddy McClellan, Christina Bretschneider

Printed and bound by Malaysia (CTP-VVP)

Grammar Starter Level Workbook

Contents

Unit 1	Sentence construction 1	page 2
Unit 2	Sentence construction 2	page 4
Unit 3	Sentence construction 3	page 5
Unit 4	Using full stops	page 6
Unit 5	Capital letters	page 8
Unit 6	Word order in sentences	page 10
Unit 7	Uses of capital letters	page 12
Unit 8	Linking words	page 14
Unit 9	Organisational devices	page 15
Unit 10	Question marks	page 16
Unit 12	Exclamation marks	page 18
Unit 13	Commas	page 19
Unit 14	Speech marks	page 20
Unit 15	Speech bubbles	page 22
Unit 16	Ways of presenting text	page 23
Unit 18	Commas in lists	page 24
Unit 19	Regular past tense	page 26
Unit 20	Tricky past tenses!	page 28
Unit 21	Does my sentence make sense?	page 30
Unit 22	Question words	page 32

Sentence construction 1

🔑 Key idea

A verb is a "doing" or a "being" word. All sentences need a verb to say what is happening.

Who's doing what?

Look at each of these pictures and write the verb which shows what the person is doing in each one. Choose the verbs from the box. *(1 mark for each correct answer)*

| singing | running | fishing | swimming | drinking |
| cooking | crying | writing | eating | kicking |

1.
2.
3.
4.
5.
6.
7.
8.
9.
10.

Finish the sentence

Choose a verb to complete each sentence.

(1 mark for each correct answer)

| swam   drove   ran |
| danced   watched |
| barked   washed |
| played   drilled   changed |

1 The lady _____ for the bus.
2 Tariq _____ at the disco.
3 Tariq _____ T.V. after school.
4 The dog _____ at the old man.
5 Tariq _____ his hands.
6 The magician _____ a bird into a rabbit!
7 The dentist _____ Tariq's tooth.
8 Tariq and Adam _____ football in the park.
9 Adam _____ in the pool.
10 Tariq's dad _____ to school in his new car.

Spot the verb!

Some of these sentences have a verb missing! Try to spot them, putting a tick or a cross after each sentence. Tick if the verb is there or put a cross if the verb is missing. *(1 mark for each correct answer)*

1 Tariq shut the door.   6 Jill watched the film.
2 Mary the car.   7 Tariq cut the string.
3 Amy the park.   8 He the new cards.
4 I saw a bird.   9 The cup is red.
5 The boy seven.   10 Tariq read two books.

Unit 2 Sentence construction 2

🔑 Key idea

A sentence is a group of words which carries a meaning.
Sentences must make sense.

    Amy walked to school.

This sentence tells us how Amy got to school. It makes sense and is a complete idea.

Correct it!

These sentences have got mixed up. Underline the wrong word and write the correct one at the end of the sentence. *(3 marks for each correct answer)*

1 The cat was barking. _____
2 The bear was very tiny. _____
3 An ant is big and furry. _____
4 The dog drank the milk. _____
5 A rabbit lives in a swamp. _____
6 A crocodile lives in a hutch. _____

Get it right!

These sentences do not make sense. Change the word in bold so that the sentence makes sense. *(2 marks for each correct answer)*

1 Amy **are** a very nice girl. _____
2 Tariq **have** a cat. _____
3 The dogs **has** long tails. _____
4 Dad **like** ice cream. _____
5 The **shoe** were too tight. _____
6 I think Adam **are** a very kind boy. _____

Unit 3 Sentence construction 3

Key idea

Sentences have a subject and an object.
Sentences must be clear and make sense.
The subject tells us 'who' or 'what' the sentence is about. The subject goes with the verb. The object of a sentence is the person or thing the subject is doing something to.

Who's doing what?

The subject of these sentences is missing.
Write in the subject for each one. Use the words in the box to help you. *(3 marks for each correct answer)*

1 The _____ sat in his kennel.
2 The _____ played with her kittens.
3 The _____ read a story in Assembly.
4 The _____ ate a carrot.
5 A _____ flew onto the tree.

| dog teacher |
| rabbit |
| cat bird |

Finish the sentence

The object in each of these sentences is missing. Write in the object for each one. Use the words in the box to help you.

(3 marks for each correct answer)

1 The boy batted the _____.
2 The postman dropped a _____.
3 The dog found a long, white _____.
4 The cow chewed the _____.
5 The bird sat on the _____.

| letter bone |
| ball grass |
| branch |

Unit 4 Using full stops

Key idea

A full stop marks the end of a sentence. It shows the reader where one idea ends.

Amy wanted a new book. She went to the shops to buy one. Two full stops are used, as there are two ideas, each in their own sentence.

Spot the stop!

Look at these sentences. The full stop is in the wrong place. Cross it out and put it in the right place. *(1 mark for each correct answer)*

1 Adam. went to the shops
2 Amy saw. her sister
3 The man walked. into town
4 Tariq played with his friend. Sam
5 The lady had two. bags of shopping
6 Adam helped in the. garden
7 The. cow was in the field.
8 Amy flew her. kite on Saturday
9 John saw the. fireworks
10 The lady sang a beautiful. song

6

Find the sentence

Some words have been added to the ends of these sentences. Put in the full stop to show where the sentence should end and cross out the extra words! *(1 mark for each correct answer)*

For example: John was happy. ~~doors shops~~

1 Tariq enjoyed his party waits says
2 Amy watched the film snow open
3 The doctor went to see Adam shake David Hamid
4 The shops were very busy time cooking frosty
5 John went fishing with his dad baby shoes Tuesday
6 Amy saw a magic show ties paper poster
7 The King spoke to the crowd strange book cows
8 Yesterday Tariq built a model glass coats
9 The owl hooted in the night cards
10 It was a very hot day windows newspaper

Correct the story

There are ten missing full stops in this short story. Put in the full stops so that the story makes sense. *(1 mark for each correct answer)*

Amy was reading in her bedroom Her mum came in and asked her if she wanted to go to the fair Amy was so excited Later that afternoon Amy and her mum set off When they got there Amy saw the dodgems Amy wanted to have a go Her mum agreed and she had two rides Then Amy saw the ghost train Amy was a bit scared but she had a ride It was lots of fun

Unit 5: Capital letters

🔑 Key idea

Capital letters are used to show the start of a sentence and to identify proper nouns, such as names of people.

Everyone saw the clowns and Freddy was the biggest clown of all. **Everyone** starts with a capital letter as it begins the sentence. **Freddy** begins with a capital letter as it is a name.

Send in the clowns!

Write out the names of the clowns. Each name should start with a capital letter. *(1 mark for each correct answer)*

| coco | daisy | billy | sidney | freddy |
| joey | archie | peggy | winston | smartie |

_____   _____

_____   _____

_____   _____

_____   _____

A capital idea!

Write out each sentence remembering to start with a capital letter.

(1 mark for each correct answer)

1. the tent was very big. _____
2. joey had orange hair. _____
3. the tickets cost £3.50. _____
4. a lady was selling ice creams. _____
5. the clowns made us laugh. _____
6. i laughed at the clowns. _____
7. freddy fell off his chair! _____
8. mum got me a clown badge. _____
9. it was an exciting show. _____
10. i would like to see it again. _____

What happened next?

Write out five sentences about some funny things the clowns might have done. Remember to start each one with a capital letter. Use these words to help you: clown, mess, threw, pies, water, car, squirted and crash. *(2 marks for each correct sentence)*

_____

_____

_____

_____

_____

Unit 6 — Word order in sentences

Key idea

Each sentence has a subject and an object. Words in a sentence must be in the correct order to make sense.

   An alien flew down to Earth.

This sentence makes sense. The words are in the correct order. The sentence tells us something. It conveys an idea.

Alien message

Translate this alien message by putting the words into the correct order in each sentence. *(2 marks for each correct sentence)*

Venus from we send greetings. Peace we come in. friends your are we. Chocolate like we. Large is our very spaceship.

_____

_____

_____

Alien objects

Complete this message from the aliens by putting in an object for each sentence. *(1 mark for each correct answer)*

We have read all your _____

We have tasted your _____

Our spaceship landed on the _____

We write with long _____

We would like to eat some _____

Our planet crashed into _____

We have looked at your _____

Our computer has tested your _____

We are excited by your _____

Our troops have been into the _____

Write to the aliens!

Make up your own message for the aliens. You will need to write out five short sentences, changing the word order so that it does not make sense to humans. Make sure you include all the words you will need in each sentence. Make sure each sentence has a subject. *(2 marks for each correct sentence)*

For example:

Where have you come from? = Come from have where you?

_____

_____

_____

_____

Capital letters

Key idea

Capital letters are used to show the start of a sentence, and to identify proper nouns – names of people, places, titles and times.

Capitalise!

Write these words below, so that each one starts with a capital letter. *(1 mark for each correct answer)*

may _____   rome _____

i _____   fred _____

paul _____   tuesday _____

february _____   sally _____

sunday _____   august _____

Choose a word!

Write eight words that need to start with a capital letter. You might choose the names of people, places, days or months of the year. *(1 mark for each correct answer)*

_____   _____

_____   _____

_____   _____

_____   _____

Now write the name of your favourite book or story. *(2 marks)*

_____

Which is right?

Adam has got mixed up and written every word below with a capital letter! Copy it out correctly, keeping only the correct capitals. *(0.5 mark for each correction)*

On Sunday I Saw My Friend Sam. He Has A Dog Called Scruffy. We Took Scruffy To The Park On Sunshine Street. It Was Lots Of Fun! We Will Go Again Next Sunday.

_____

_____

_____

_____

Unit 8 Linking words

Key idea

We can join short sentences together to make longer, more interesting sentences. We use link words like AND, SO or BUT.

    The lion was hungry. The lion ate some meat.
    = The lion was hungry so he ate some meat.

We do not need the second "The lion" as we know he is the subject of the sentence.

Zoo report

Amy wrote a report of her trip to the zoo. Join these pairs of sentences together using "and". *(3 marks for each correct sentence)*

1   I put on my coat. I went to the zoo. _____
2   I carried my camera. I took photos. _____
3   I saw the zebras. I saw the chimps. _____
4   I fed the rabbits. I fed the ducks. _____
5   The chimps were noisy. They were funny. _____

All mixed up!

Choose from "and", "so", "because" or "but" to join these sentences. *(3 marks for each correct sentence)*

1   I am going home. It is too late to go to the zoo. _____
2   You are helping me. She is not. _____
3   I love the chimps. They are funny animals. _____
4   I ate an ice cream. I ate a hot dog. _____
5   I wanted to buy a T-shirt. I didn't have enough money. _____

Unit 9 Organisational devices

🔑 Key idea

We use short sentences, letters, numbers or bullet points and pictures to set out instructions.

Set it out!

Write out these instructions so that they are easy to follow.
(15 marks)

Giving your puppy a bath. First, fill the bath half way with warm water. Put your puppy in the bath and wash it with soap and water. Rinse the puppy carefully. Lift your puppy out of the bath. Dry your puppy with a towel and brush its coat.

_____   _____

_____   _____

_____   _____

Make a snowman

These instructions are mixed up. Read them carefully and put a letter from "a" to "f" next to each one to order them. *(15 marks)*

a.   Firstly, roll a large ball of snow.
___ Finally, put a hat on his head and a scarf around his neck.
___ Roll a smaller ball and put it on top for a head.
___ Push in two sticks for arms and put gloves on for hands.
___ Add two stones and a carrot to the smaller ball for a face.

Unit 10: Question marks

Key idea

A question mark is used to show a question.
It comes at the end of the question.
You do not need a full stop after a question mark.

> What is your name?
>
> How old are you?

These are both questions, as they need an answer.

Here we go!

**Add question marks to the end of these five questions.
Make sure you form the question mark carefully.** *(1 mark for each correct answer)*

1. Is it a long trip
2. Are you going by plane
3. Do you have two bags
4. Will the plane land in Glasgow
5. Is this a jumbo jet

Find that question!

Look through one of your reading books and write down five questions that you find in the story. Remember to begin each with a capital letter and put a question mark at the end.
(10 marks)

_____

_____

_____

_____

_____

Interview a pilot!

Here are five answers a pilot gave, but what were the questions? Look at the answers and write the question you think he was asked. *(3 marks for each correct question)*

_____

I have been a pilot for 4 years.

_____

My favourite airport is in Paris.

_____

Yes, I do like my uniform.

_____

I wanted to be a pilot when I was young.

_____

I was born in Manchester.

Unit 12 Exclamation marks

🔑 Key idea

We use exclamation marks to show that something scary, exciting or surprising has happened. They are also used to show that someone in a story is shouting or something is loud.

Read the signs!

These signs have their exclamation marks missing. Copy them carefully and add the exclamation marks. *(2 marks for each one)*

DANGER _____

Falling Rocks _____

Do not swim here _____

Private _____

Do not enter _____

The spooky castle

There are ten exclamation marks missing from this short story. Read it carefully and put them in. *(1 mark for each correct answer)*

Aneena went into the old, spooky castle. CRASH. The old clock fell off the wall all by itself. Aneena thought it must be a ghost. THUD. The door slammed shut by itself. BOOM. WHOOSH. A cannon on the roof went off. Aneena was very scared, so she pulled the door but it was stuck.

Finish the story!

Write out the end of Aneena's story. *(10 marks)*

Unit 13 Commas

Key idea

Commas are used to add extra information or to create a pause. They break up longer sentences into smaller parts.

Quickly, Davina locked the door!

Exciting sentences!

Complete these sentences in an exciting way, by finishing each sentence after the comma. *(3 marks for each correct sentence)*

Suddenly, _____

Just at that moment, _____

All at once, _____

The door slowly opened, _____

Although it was dark, _____

Finally, _____

Commas in pairs!

Place the commas where you think extra information has been added to each sentence. *(2 marks for each correct sentence)*

The clock which was very old did not work.

Davina who was wearing a red dress hid behind the red curtains.

The rain which had been pouring all day finally stopped.

Davina in her loudest voice shouted from behind the curtains!

Everyone including Davina's mum was very surprised!

Everyone including Davina had to walk home through the rain.

Unit 14 Speech marks

Key idea

We use speech marks to show when someone is speaking.

"Are you Fred the Robot?" asked the Captain.

What the Captain said is put inside speech marks.

What did you say?

Write some speech for each of these characters inside the speech marks. Remember question marks or exclamation marks go INSIDE the speech marks. *(2 marks for each correct sentence)*

"_____" asked the teacher.

"_____," called Mum.

"_____" shouted the policeman.

"_____" laughed the clown.

"_____" asked the shopkeeper.

Who said that?

It is important if we're writing a story with more than one character in it to say who is speaking. Read these lines of speech and write down who might have said them. *(1 mark for each correct answer)*

"It's time you did your homework!" called _____

"It's time for Assembly," said _____

"Hand over your money!" shouted _____

"I'll turn you into a frog!" cackled _____

"Can I help you, Sir?" asked _____

"You've got a broken arm," said _____

Where do they go?

The speech marks in this story are in the wrong place. Cross them out and put them in the right places. *(1 mark for each correct answer)*

Can I help you? "said the lady at the counter". Yes, "please," replied Carl. "He wanted to buy" a new bike. How much is that one? he asked. "It's £100, replied the lady." Oh dear, said "Carl", I'll have to save up my "pocket money!" Carl left the shop, but he would "get that bike, one day."

Speech bubbles

Key idea

A speech bubble is used to show who is speaking and what they have said. Speech bubbles are used in pictures, cartoons, posters and information texts. We do not use speech marks inside a speech bubble.

Perfect pets!

Write what each pet is saying in the correct speech bubble.

(5 marks for each correct answer)

"I'll fetch that stick!"   "I've laid you an egg!"   "Can I have some milk?"

Look after your pets!

Here is Jaswinder, the vet. Write in her tips for looking after your pet. There are some clues to help you in the pictures.

(15 marks)

Ways of presenting texts – BLOCK CAPITALS

Key idea

We use BLOCK CAPITALS when writing to show that something is important, scary, exciting or dangerous.
They also mark someone is shouting or giving an instruction or a warning.

STOP!   "Don't go in THERE!"

A capital idea

Write out the alphabet in BLOCK CAPITALS.
Make sure each letter is formed correctly! *(0.5 mark for each correct letter and 1 mark for the correct order)*

The right sign

Write out these signs using BLOCK CAPITALS. Then write five more of your own. *(2 marks for each correct sign)*

Beware of the dog.

High Tides.

Open.

Unit 18 Commas in lists

🔑 Key idea

Commas are used to separate items in a list.

> Joe put a pencil, a rubber, a sharpener and an apple into his bag.

The last two items in a list are joined by "and" to show it is the end of this list.

Comma collections

Put the missing commas into these lists. *(1 mark for each correct comma)*

Apple orange grape and pear.
Tea coffee milk and water.
Pencil felt-tip crayon and pen.
Card envelope letter and stamp.
Plate saucer jug and cup.

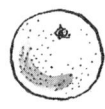

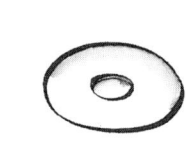

What is missing?

Write out these lists, putting in the missing commas. Remember to place an "and" between the last two items. *(1 mark for each correct comma and "and")*

Drum guitar piano recorder.
Hammer saw nail screw.
Oak ash elm willow pine.

What do you like?

Finish these lists. *(2 marks for each list)*

I like to drink _____ _____ and _____.
I don't like _____ _____ ___ _____.
I like to play _____ _____ ___ _____.
I wish I had a _____ _____ ___ _____.
I would like to go to _____ _____ ___ _____.

Unit 19 Regular past tense

Key idea

We use the past tense to say when something has already happened. Many verbs make the past tense by adding **ed**.

I wash my face – it is happening now; it is the PRESENT TENSE.

I wash**ed** my face – it happened some time ago; it is the PAST TENSE.

Back in time!

Write out these verbs turning them into the past tense by adding **ed**. *(1 mark for each correct answer)*

pull	_____	jump	_____
play	_____	push	_____
look	_____	call	_____
shout	_____	brush	_____
watch	_____	turn	_____

Drop the 'e' and add 'ed'

Make these verbs into the past tense by dropping the e and adding **ed**. *(0.5 mark for each correct answer)*

race	_____	skate	_____
cuddle	_____	change	_____
smile	_____	wipe	_____
wiggle	_____	hope	_____

Time for a story

Change the verbs so this story is in the past tense. *(1 mark for each correct past tense and 1 for each sentence written out correctly)*

Last Tuesday, Sophie and I play our favourite game, Tug of War. I pull very hard. I watch the rope carefully. I move my feet slowly. I call to the winner. I enjoy this game!

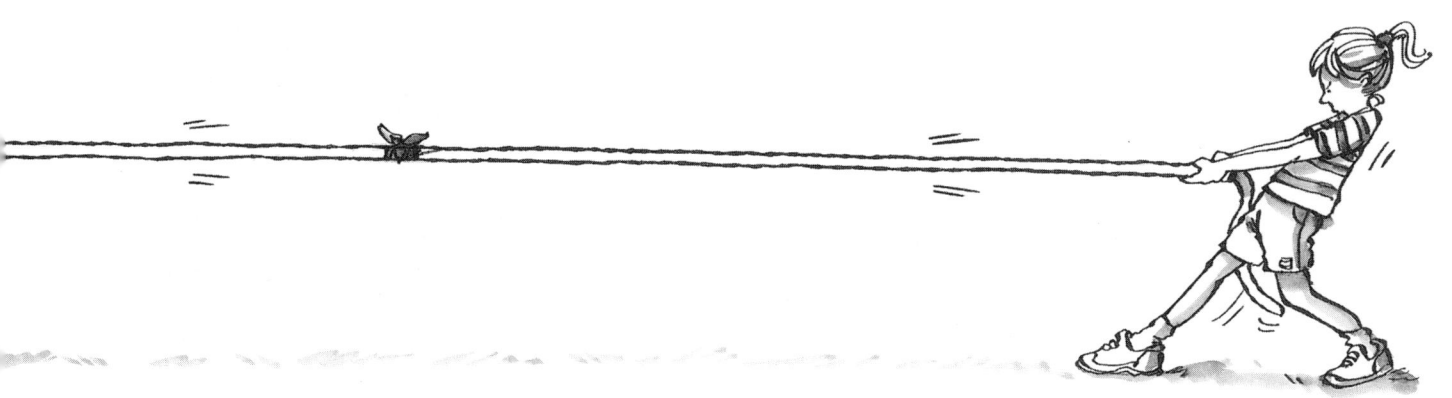

Unit 20 Tricky past tenses

Key idea

Not all verbs add **ed** to put them into the past. Verbs which do not are called **irregular** verbs.

I make a model = I made a model.

We can check by adding **ed**. If it doesn't sound right, then it must be an irregular verb.

All in the past!

Write these past tenses in the present tense. *(1 mark for each correct answer)*

For example, saw = see

went = _____
took = _____
drove = _____
came = _____
ate = _____
fought = _____
grew = _____
won = _____
slept = _____
hid = _____

Verb detective!

Underline the verbs which do not use **ed** to make the past tense. Check by saying each verb with **ed** at the end. *(0.5 mark for each correct answer)*

play	see	make	fly	wish	run	call	sit
						give	
drink	turn	eat	write	catch	jump	dig	tell
paint	build	munch	ride	pick	hold	go	
chase	sing	have	shout	ring	wear		

All mixed up!

Rewrite this story, so that it uses the correct past tense.
(2 marks for each correct tense)

Yesterday Amit **go** to the seaside. He **takes** his swimming kit and he **swimmed** in the sea. He **eat** an ice cream and **writed** a postcard to his friend.

_____

_____

_____

_____

_____

_____

_____

Unit 21

Does my sentence make sense?

Key idea

Sentences must make sense and all their parts must work together.

The Princess wore his tiara = The Princess wore her tiara.

This sentence doesn't make sense as the "Princess" is wearing "his" tiara. Each part of the sentence must "agree".

We must also check that the subject and the verb "agree". The King were sad = The King was sad.

Get it right!

Choose the correct word to finish each sentence. *(1 mark for each correct answer)*

1. The King wore _____ crown. (his/her)
2. The Queen wore _____ jewels. (his/her)
3. The people _____ happy. (was/were)
4. The castle _____ very big. (is/are)
5. There _____ lots of flowers in the garden. (was/were)

Is this correct?

Underline the word that is wrong. Put the correct word in the space. *(2 marks for each correct sentence)*

1. The Prince were tired. _____
2. The boys was friends. _____
3. The King like to eat sweets. _____
4. The Queen give the Prince a pet. _____
5. It are a kitten. _____

The prince's cat

Correct the Prince's mistakes in his pet report. Check that each sentence makes sense! *(3 marks for each correct answer)*

My cat like to chase mice. It have very soft fur. There is lots of rats in the castle and my cat chases it! I think my cat are wonderful.

Question words

Key idea

When we write a question we often start with a question word.
A question word asks a question all by itself.
Who? Why? When? Where? What? How? These are all question words.
We always put a question mark at the end of a question.

Who or how?

Put in the correct question word to finish these questions.
(2 marks for each correct sentence)

1 _____ did you get here?
2 _____ told you that?
3 _____ old are you?
4 _____ did you do that?
5 _____ is your favourite footballer?

Interview time!

Write out a series of questions that you would like to ask a friend, your teacher or a member of your family. Use the question words given to start off each question. Make sure each one ends with a question mark. *(20 marks)*

How _____
Where _____
When _____
Who _____
What _____

Key Grammar is a brand new resource, specifically planned to cover all the key grammar objectives in self-contained units of work. The pupil books feature:

- **clear, progressive units covering all key learning objectives**
- **plenty of practice and consolidation work**
- **opportunities to challenge and extend children's learning**
- **a clear mark scheme**
- **exercises in an appropriate context, with engaging illustrations**

The workbooks provide activities for additional practice, differentiation, and homework. The important language skills coverage in **Key Grammar** is complemented by two associated series:
Key Comprehension and **Key Spelling** – up-to-date and engaging resources which reinforce key teaching points and enable children to practise, consolidate and extend their learning. For further information about **Key Comprehension** and **Key Spelling** call our Customer Services Department on **(+44) (0)1865 888000**.

ISBN 978-0-602206-79-6

Author: Chris Wardle

Ginn
Halley Court, Jordan Hill, Oxford OX2 8EJ
a division of Harcourt Education Limited

www.myprimary.co.uk
Help and support for teachers plus the widest range of education solutions

Ginn is a registered trademark of Harcourt Education Limited

© Harcourt Education Limited 2005

This book is copyright and reproduction of the whole or part without the publishers' written permission is prohibited.

Key Grammar Workbook Starter Level
ISBN: 978 0602 20679 6
Starter Level Easy Order Pack: 978 0602 20621 5
Starter Level Workbook 6 Pack: 978 0602 20643 7

First published 2005

20 19 18 17 16
15 14

Cover illustration by Pet Gotohda
Cover design by Tom Cole
Designed by Nicki Wise, Te Marama Design
Illustrations by Andrea Pretrlik Huseinovic, Maddy McClellan, Christina Bretschneider

Printed and bound by Malaysia (CTP-VVP)

 # Grammar Starter Level Workbook

Contents

Unit 1	Sentence construction 1	page 2
Unit 2	Sentence construction 2	page 4
Unit 3	Sentence construction 3	page 5
Unit 4	Using full stops	page 6
Unit 5	Capital letters	page 8
Unit 6	Word order in sentences	page 10
Unit 7	Uses of capital letters	page 12
Unit 8	Linking words	page 14
Unit 9	Organisational devices	page 15
Unit 10	Question marks	page 16
Unit 12	Exclamation marks	page 18
Unit 13	Commas	page 19
Unit 14	Speech marks	page 20
Unit 15	Speech bubbles	page 22
Unit 16	Ways of presenting text	page 23
Unit 18	Commas in lists	page 24
Unit 19	Regular past tense	page 26
Unit 20	Tricky past tenses!	page 28
Unit 21	Does my sentence make sense?	page 30
Unit 22	Question words	page 32

Unit 1

Sentence construction 1

🔑 Key idea

A verb is a "doing" or a "being" word. All sentences need a verb to say what is happening.

Who's doing what?

Look at each of these pictures and write the verb which shows what the person is doing in each one. Choose the verbs from the box. *(1 mark for each correct answer)*

| singing | running | fishing | swimming | drinking |
| cooking | crying | writing | eating | kicking |

1.
2.
3.
4.
5.
6.
7.
8.
9.
10.

Finish the sentence

Choose a verb to complete each sentence.

(1 mark for each correct answer)

| swam   drove   ran |
| danced   watched |
| barked   washed |
| played   drilled   changed |

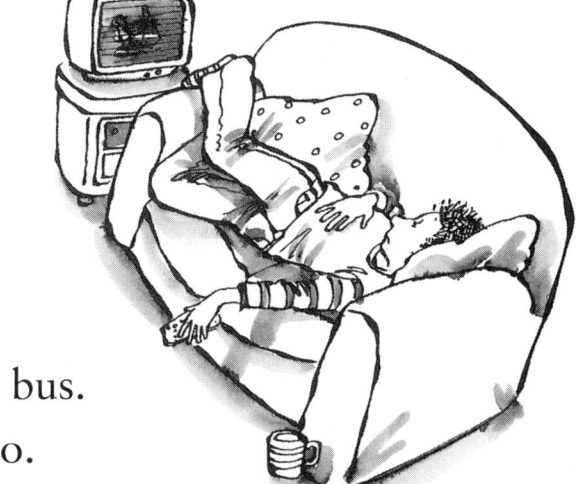

1 The lady _____ for the bus.
2 Tariq _____ at the disco.
3 Tariq _____ T.V. after school.
4 The dog _____ at the old man.
5 Tariq _____ his hands.
6 The magician _____ a bird into a rabbit!
7 The dentist _____ Tariq's tooth.
8 Tariq and Adam _____ football in the park.
9 Adam _____ in the pool.
10 Tariq's dad _____ to school in his new car.

Spot the verb!

Some of these sentences have a verb missing! Try to spot them, putting a tick or a cross after each sentence. Tick if the verb is there or put a cross if the verb is missing. *(1 mark for each correct answer)*

1 Tariq shut the door.
2 Mary the car.
3 Amy the park.
4 I saw a bird.
5 The boy seven.

6 Jill watched the film.
7 Tariq cut the string.
8 He the new cards.
9 The cup is red.
10 Tariq read two books.

Sentence construction 2

🔑 Key idea

A sentence is a group of words which carries a meaning.
Sentences must make sense.

    Amy walked to school.

This sentence tells us how Amy got to school. It makes sense and is a complete idea.

Correct it!

These sentences have got mixed up. Underline the wrong word and write the correct one at the end of the sentence. *(3 marks for each correct answer)*

1 The cat was barking. _____
2 The bear was very tiny. _____
3 An ant is big and furry. _____
4 The dog drank the milk. _____
5 A rabbit lives in a swamp. _____
6 A crocodile lives in a hutch. _____

Get it right!

These sentences do not make sense. Change the word in bold so that the sentence makes sense. *(2 marks for each correct answer)*

1 Amy **are** a very nice girl. _____
2 Tariq **have** a cat. _____
3 The dogs **has** long tails. _____
4 Dad **like** ice cream. _____
5 The **shoe** were too tight. _____
6 I think Adam **are** a very kind boy. _____

Unit 3 Sentence construction 3

Key idea

Sentences have a subject and an object.
Sentences must be clear and make sense.
The subject tells us 'who' or 'what' the sentence is about. The subject goes with the verb. The object of a sentence is the person or thing the subject is doing something to.

Who's doing what?

The subject of these sentences is missing.
Write in the subject for each one. Use the words in the box to help you. *(3 marks for each correct answer)*

1 The _____ sat in his kennel.
2 The _____ played with her kittens.
3 The _____ read a story in Assembly.
4 The _____ ate a carrot.
5 A _____ flew onto the tree.

> dog   teacher
> rabbit
> cat   bird

Finish the sentence

The object in each of these sentences is missing. Write in the object for each one. Use the words in the box to help you.

(3 marks for each correct answer)

1 The boy batted the _____.
2 The postman dropped a _____.
3 The dog found a long, white _____.
4 The cow chewed the _____.
5 The bird sat on the _____.

> letter   bone
> ball   grass
> branch

Unit 4 Using full stops

Key idea

A full stop marks the end of a sentence. It shows the reader where one idea ends.

Amy wanted a new book. She went to the shops to buy one.

Two full stops are used, as there are two ideas, each in their own sentence.

Spot the stop!

Look at these sentences. The full stop is in the wrong place. Cross it out and put it in the right place. *(1 mark for each correct answer)*

1 Adam. went to the shops
2 Amy saw. her sister
3 The man walked. into town
4 Tariq played with his friend. Sam
5 The lady had two. bags of shopping
6 Adam helped in the. garden
7 The. cow was in the field.
8 Amy flew her. kite on Saturday
9 John saw the. fireworks
10 The lady sang a beautiful. song

Find the sentence

Some words have been added to the ends of these sentences. Put in the full stop to show where the sentence should end and cross out the extra words! *(1 mark for each correct answer)*

For example: John was happy. ~~doors shops~~

1 Tariq enjoyed his party waits says
2 Amy watched the film snow open
3 The doctor went to see Adam shake David Hamid
4 The shops were very busy time cooking frosty
5 John went fishing with his dad baby shoes Tuesday
6 Amy saw a magic show ties paper poster
7 The King spoke to the crowd strange book cows
8 Yesterday Tariq built a model glass coats
9 The owl hooted in the night cards
10 It was a very hot day windows newspaper

Correct the story

There are ten missing full stops in this short story. Put in the full stops so that the story makes sense. *(1 mark for each correct answer)*

Amy was reading in her bedroom Her mum came in and asked her if she wanted to go to the fair Amy was so excited Later that afternoon Amy and her mum set off When they got there Amy saw the dodgems Amy wanted to have a go Her mum agreed and she had two rides Then Amy saw the ghost train Amy was a bit scared but she had a ride It was lots of fun

Unit 5 Capital letters

🔑 Key idea

Capital letters are used to show the start of a sentence and to identify proper nouns, such as names of people.

Everyone saw the clowns and Freddy was the biggest clown of all. **Everyone** starts with a capital letter as it begins the sentence. **Freddy** begins with a capital letter as it is a name.

Send in the clowns!

Write out the names of the clowns. Each name should start with a capital letter. *(1 mark for each correct answer)*

| coco | daisy | billy | sidney | freddy |
| joey | archie | peggy | winston | smartie |

_____ _____

_____ _____

_____ _____

_____ _____

_____ _____

A capital idea!

Write out each sentence remembering to start with a capital letter.

(1 mark for each correct answer)

1. the tent was very big. _____
2. joey had orange hair. _____
3. the tickets cost £3.50. _____
4. a lady was selling ice creams. _____
5. the clowns made us laugh. _____
6. i laughed at the clowns. _____
7. freddy fell off his chair! _____
8. mum got me a clown badge. _____
9. it was an exciting show. _____
10. i would like to see it again. _____

What happened next?

Write out five sentences about some funny things the clowns might have done. Remember to start each one with a capital letter. Use these words to help you: clown, mess, threw, pies, water, car, squirted and crash. *(2 marks for each correct sentence)*

_____

_____

_____

_____

_____

Unit 6

Word order in sentences

Key idea

Each sentence has a subject and an object. Words in a sentence must be in the correct order to make sense.

> An alien flew down to Earth.

This sentence makes sense. The words are in the correct order. The sentence tells us something. It conveys an idea.

Alien message

Translate this alien message by putting the words into the correct order in each sentence. *(2 marks for each correct sentence)*

Venus from we send greetings. Peace we come in. friends your are we. Chocolate like we. Large is our very spaceship.

_____

_____

_____

Alien objects

Complete this message from the aliens by putting in an object for each sentence. *(1 mark for each correct answer)*

We have read all your _____

We have tasted your _____

Our spaceship landed on the _____

We write with long _____

We would like to eat some _____

Our planet crashed into _____

We have looked at your _____

Our computer has tested your _____

We are excited by your _____

Our troops have been into the _____

Write to the aliens!

Make up your own message for the aliens. You will need to write out five short sentences, changing the word order so that it does not make sense to humans. Make sure you include all the words you will need in each sentence. Make sure each sentence has a subject. *(2 marks for each correct sentence)*

For example:

Where have you come from? = Come from have where you?

_____

_____

_____

_____

Unit 7 Capital letters

🔑 Key idea

Capital letters are used to show the start of a sentence, and to identify proper nouns – names of people, places, titles and times.

Capitalise!

Write these words below, so that each one starts with a capital letter. *(1 mark for each correct answer)*

may _____   rome _____

i _____   fred _____

paul _____   tuesday _____

february _____   sally _____

sunday _____   august _____

Choose a word!

Write eight words that need to start with a capital letter. You might choose the names of people, places, days or months of the year. *(1 mark for each correct answer)*

_____   _____

_____   _____

_____   _____

_____   _____

Now write the name of your favourite book or story. *(2 marks)*

_____

Which is right?

Adam has got mixed up and written every word below with a capital letter! Copy it out correctly, keeping only the correct capitals. *(0.5 mark for each correction)*

On Sunday I Saw My Friend Sam. He Has A Dog Called Scruffy. We Took Scruffy To The Park On Sunshine Street. It Was Lots Of Fun! We Will Go Again Next Sunday.

_____

_____

_____

_____

Unit 8 Linking words

🔑 Key idea

We can join short sentences together to make longer, more interesting sentences. We use link words like AND, SO or BUT.

The lion was hungry. The lion ate some meat.
= The lion was hungry so he ate some meat.

We do not need the second "The lion" as we know he is the subject of the sentence.

Zoo report

Amy wrote a report of her trip to the zoo. Join these pairs of sentences together using "and". *(3 marks for each correct sentence)*

1 I put on my coat. I went to the zoo. _____
2 I carried my camera. I took photos. _____
3 I saw the zebras. I saw the chimps. _____
4 I fed the rabbits. I fed the ducks. _____
5 The chimps were noisy. They were funny. _____

All mixed up!

Choose from "and", "so", "because" or "but" to join these sentences. *(3 marks for each correct sentence)*

1 I am going home. It is too late to go to the zoo. _____
2 You are helping me. She is not. _____
3 I love the chimps. They are funny animals. _____
4 I ate an ice cream. I ate a hot dog. _____
5 I wanted to buy a T-shirt. I didn't have enough money. _____

Unit 9 Organisational devices

🔑 Key idea

We use short sentences, letters, numbers or bullet points and pictures to set out instructions.

Set it out!

Write out these instructions so that they are easy to follow.
(15 marks)

Giving your puppy a bath. First, fill the bath half way with warm water. Put your puppy in the bath and wash it with soap and water. Rinse the puppy carefully. Lift your puppy out of the bath. Dry your puppy with a towel and brush its coat.

_____   _____

_____   _____

_____   _____

Make a snowman

These instructions are mixed up. Read them carefully and put a letter from "a" to "f" next to each one to order them. *(15 marks)*

a. Firstly, roll a large ball of snow.
___ Finally, put a hat on his head and a scarf around his neck.
___ Roll a smaller ball and put it on top for a head.
___ Push in two sticks for arms and put gloves on for hands.
___ Add two stones and a carrot to the smaller ball for a face.

Unit 10 Question marks

Key idea

A question mark is used to show a question.
It comes at the end of the question.
You do not need a full stop after a question mark.

> What is your name?
>
> How old are you?

These are both questions, as they need an answer.

Here we go!

Add question marks to the end of these five questions.
Make sure you form the question mark carefully. *(1 mark for each correct answer)*

1 Is it a long trip
2 Are you going by plane
3 Do you have two bags
4 Will the plane land in Glasgow
5 Is this a jumbo jet

Find that question!

Look through one of your reading books and write down five questions that you find in the story. Remember to begin each with a capital letter and put a question mark at the end.
(10 marks)

_____

_____

_____

_____

_____

Interview a pilot!

Here are five answers a pilot gave, but what were the questions? Look at the answers and write the question you think he was asked. *(3 marks for each correct question)*

_____

I have been a pilot for 4 years.

_____

My favourite airport is in Paris.

_____

Yes, I do like my uniform.

_____

I wanted to be a pilot when I was young.

_____

I was born in Manchester.

Unit 12 Exclamation marks

🔑 Key idea

We use exclamation marks to show that something scary, exciting or surprising has happened. They are also used to show that someone in a story is shouting or something is loud.

Read the signs!

These signs have their exclamation marks missing. Copy them carefully and add the exclamation marks. *(2 marks for each one)*

DANGER _____

Falling Rocks _____

Do not swim here _____

Private _____

Do not enter _____

The spooky castle

There are ten exclamation marks missing from this short story. Read it carefully and put them in. *(1 mark for each correct answer)*

Aneena went into the old, spooky castle. CRASH. The old clock fell off the wall all by itself. Aneena thought it must be a ghost. THUD. The door slammed shut by itself. BOOM. WHOOSH. A cannon on the roof went off. Aneena was very scared, so she pulled the door but it was stuck.

Finish the story!

Write out the end of Aneena's story. *(10 marks)*

Commas

🔑 Key idea

Commas are used to add extra information or to create a pause. They break up longer sentences into smaller parts.

Quickly, Davina locked the door!

Exciting sentences!

Complete these sentences in an exciting way, by finishing each sentence after the comma. *(3 marks for each correct sentence)*

Suddenly, _____

Just at that moment, _____

All at once, _____

The door slowly opened, _____

Although it was dark, _____

Finally, _____

Commas in pairs!

Place the commas where you think extra information has been added to each sentence. *(2 marks for each correct sentence)*

The clock which was very old did not work.

Davina who was wearing a red dress hid behind the red curtains.

The rain which had been pouring all day finally stopped.

Davina in her loudest voice shouted from behind the curtains!

Everyone including Davina's mum was very surprised!

Everyone including Davina had to walk home through the rain.

Speech marks

Key idea

We use speech marks to show when someone is speaking.

"Are you Fred the Robot?" asked the Captain.

What the Captain said is put inside speech marks.

What did you say?

Write some speech for each of these characters inside the speech marks. Remember question marks or exclamation marks go INSIDE the speech marks. *(2 marks for each correct sentence)*

"_____" asked the teacher.

"_____," called Mum.

"_____" shouted the policeman.

"_____" laughed the clown.

"_____" asked the shopkeeper.

Who said that?

It is important if we're writing a story with more than one character in it to say who is speaking. Read these lines of speech and write down who might have said them. *(1 mark for each correct answer)*

"It's time you did your homework!" called _____

"It's time for Assembly," said _____

"Hand over your money!" shouted _____

"I'll turn you into a frog!" cackled _____

"Can I help you, Sir?" asked _____

"You've got a broken arm," said _____

Where do they go?

The speech marks in this story are in the wrong place. Cross them out and put them in the right places. *(1 mark for each correct answer)*

Can I help you? "said the lady at the counter". Yes, "please," replied Carl. "He wanted to buy" a new bike. How much is that one? he asked. "It's £100, replied the lady." Oh dear, said "Carl", I'll have to save up my "pocket money!" Carl left the shop, but he would "get that bike, one day."

Speech bubbles

🔑 Key idea

A speech bubble is used to show who is speaking and what they have said. Speech bubbles are used in pictures, cartoons, posters and information texts. We do not use speech marks inside a speech bubble.

Perfect pets!

Write what each pet is saying in the correct speech bubble.

(5 marks for each correct answer)

"I'll fetch that stick!"   "I've laid you an egg!"   "Can I have some milk?"

Look after your pets!

Here is Jaswinder, the vet. Write in her tips for looking after your pet. There are some clues to help you in the pictures.

(15 marks)

Unit 16: Ways of presenting texts – BLOCK CAPITALS

Key idea

We use BLOCK CAPITALS when writing to show that something is important, scary, exciting or dangerous.
They also mark someone is shouting or giving an instruction or a warning.
STOP!   "Don't go in THERE!"

A capital idea

**Write out the alphabet in BLOCK CAPITALS.
Make sure each letter is formed correctly!** *(0.5 mark for each correct letter and 1 mark for the correct order)*

___ ___ ___ ___ ___ ___

___ ___ ___ ___ ___ ___

___ ___ ___ ___ ___ ___

___ ___ ___ ___ ___ ___

___ ___

The right sign

Write out these signs using BLOCK CAPITALS. Then write five more of your own. *(2 marks for each correct sign)*

Beware of the dog.   _____

_____   _____

High Tides.   _____

_____   _____

Open.   _____

_____

Unit 18 Commas in lists

Key idea

Commas are used to separate items in a list.

Joe put a pencil, a rubber, a sharpener and an apple into his bag.

The last two items in a list are joined by "and" to show it is the end of this list.

Comma collections

Put the missing commas into these lists. *(1 mark for each correct comma)*

Apple orange grape and pear.
Tea coffee milk and water.
Pencil felt-tip crayon and pen.
Card envelope letter and stamp.
Plate saucer jug and cup.

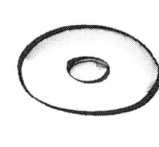

What is missing?

Write out these lists, putting in the missing commas. Remember to place an "and" between the last two items. *(1 mark for each correct comma and "and")*

Drum guitar piano recorder.

Hammer saw nail screw.

Oak ash elm willow pine.

What do you like?

Finish these lists. *(2 marks for each list)*

I like to drink _____ _____ and _____.

I don't like _____ _____ ___ _____.

I like to play _____ _____ ___ _____.

I wish I had a _____ _____ ___ _____.

I would like to go to _____ _____ ___ _____.

Unit 19 Regular past tense

🔑 Key idea

We use the past tense to say when something has already happened. Many verbs make the past tense by adding **ed**.

I wash my face – it is happening now; it is the PRESENT TENSE.

I wash**ed** my face – it happened some time ago; it is the PAST TENSE.

Back in time!

Write out these verbs turning them into the past tense by adding **ed**. *(1 mark for each correct answer)*

pull	_____	jump	_____
play	_____	push	_____
look	_____	call	_____
shout	_____	brush	_____
watch	_____	turn	_____

Drop the 'e' and add 'ed'

Make these verbs into the past tense by dropping the e and adding **ed**. *(0.5 mark for each correct answer)*

race	_____	skate	_____
cuddle	_____	change	_____
smile	_____	wipe	_____
wiggle	_____	hope	_____

Time for a story

Change the verbs so this story is in the past tense. *(1 mark for each correct past tense and 1 for each sentence written out correctly)*

Last Tuesday, Sophie and I play our favourite game, Tug of War. I pull very hard. I watch the rope carefully. I move my feet slowly. I call to the winner. I enjoy this game!

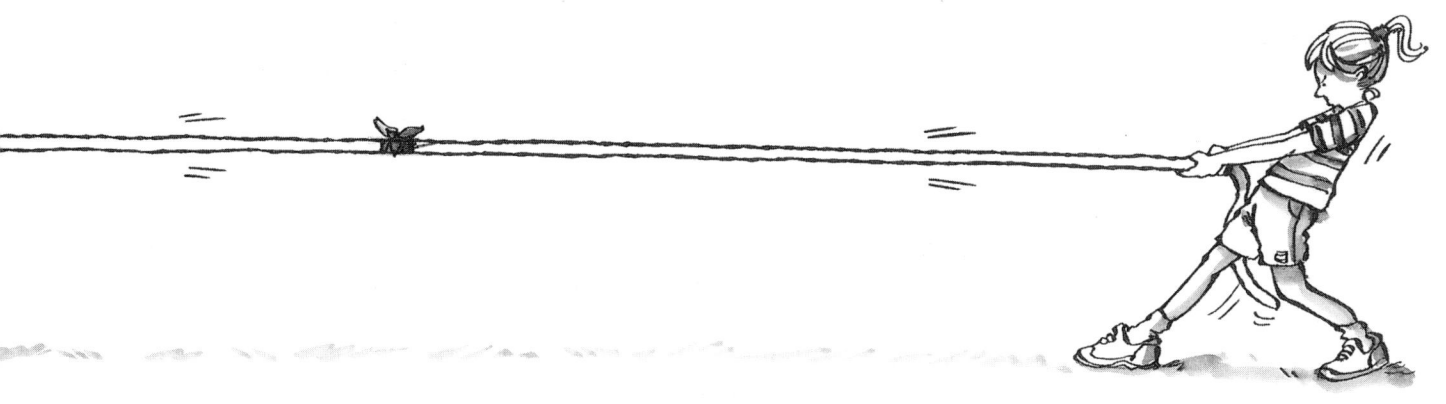

# unit 20
Tricky past tenses

 **Key idea** ··

Not all verbs add **ed** to put them into the past. Verbs which do not are called **irregular** verbs.

I make a model = I made a model.

We can check by adding **ed**. If it doesn't sound right, then it must be an irregular verb.

All in the past! ··

Write these past tenses in the present tense. *(1 mark for each correct answer)*

For example, saw = see

went = _____
took = _____
drove = _____
came = _____
ate = _____
fought = _____
grew = _____
won = _____
slept = _____
hid = _____

Verb detective!

Underline the verbs which do not use ed to make the past tense. Check by saying each verb with ed at the end. *(0.5 mark for each correct answer)*

play	see	make	fly	wish	run	call	give	sit
drink	turn	eat	write	catch	jump	dig	tell	
paint	build	munch	ride	pick	hold	go		
chase	sing	have	shout	ring	wear			

All mixed up!

Rewrite this story, so that it uses the correct past tense.
(2 marks for each correct tense)

Yesterday Amit **go** to the seaside. He **takes** his swimming kit and he **swimmed** in the sea. He **eat** an ice cream and **writed** a postcard to his friend.

_____

_____

_____

_____

_____

_____

_____

Unit 21 Does my sentence make sense?

🔑 Key idea

Sentences must make sense and all their parts must work together.

The Princess wore his tiara = The Princess wore her tiara.

This sentence doesn't make sense as the "Princess" is wearing "his" tiara. Each part of the sentence must "agree".

We must also check that the subject and the verb "agree". The King were sad = The King was sad.

Get it right!

Choose the correct word to finish each sentence. *(1 mark for each correct answer)*

1 The King wore _____ crown. (his/her)
2 The Queen wore _____ jewels. (his/her)
3 The people _____ happy. (was/were)
4 The castle _____ very big. (is/are)
5 There _____ lots of flowers in the garden. (was/were)

Is this correct?

Underline the word that is wrong. Put the correct word in the space. *(2 marks for each correct sentence)*

1 The Prince were tired. _____
2 The boys was friends. _____
3 The King like to eat sweets. _____
4 The Queen give the Prince a pet. _____
5 It are a kitten. _____

The prince's cat

Correct the Prince's mistakes in his pet report. Check that each sentence makes sense! *(3 marks for each correct answer)*

My cat like to chase mice. It have very soft fur. There is lots of rats in the castle and my cat chases it! I think my cat are wonderful.

Question words

Key idea

When we write a question we often start with a question word.
A question word asks a question all by itself.
Who? Why? When? Where? What? How? These are all question words.
We always put a question mark at the end of a question.

Who or how?

Put in the correct question word to finish these questions.

(2 marks for each correct sentence)

1 _____ did you get here?
2 _____ told you that?
3 _____ old are you?
4 _____ did you do that?
5 _____ is your favourite footballer?

Interview time!

Write out a series of questions that you would like to ask a friend, your teacher or a member of your family. Use the question words given to start off each question. Make sure each one ends with a question mark. *(20 marks)*

How _____
Where _____
When _____
Who _____
What _____

Key Grammar is a brand new resource, specifically planned to cover all the key grammar objectives in self-contained units of work. The pupil books feature:

- **clear, progressive units covering all key learning objectives**
- **plenty of practice and consolidation work**
- **opportunities to challenge and extend children's learning**
- **a clear mark scheme**
- **exercises in an appropriate context, with engaging illustrations**

The workbooks provide activities for additional practice, differentiation, and homework. The important language skills coverage in **Key Grammar** is complemented by two associated series: **Key Comprehension** and **Key Spelling** – up-to-date and engaging resources which reinforce key teaching points and enable children to practise, consolidate and extend their learning. For further information about **Key Comprehension** and **Key Spelling** call our Customer Services Department on **(+44) (0)1865 888000.**

ISBN 978-0-602206-79-6

9 780602 206796

Author: Chris Wardle

Ginn
Halley Court, Jordan Hill, Oxford OX2 8EJ
a division of Harcourt Education Limited

www.myprimary.co.uk
Help and support for teachers plus the widest range of education solutions

Ginn is a registered trademark of Harcourt Education Limited

© Harcourt Education Limited 2005

This book is copyright and reproduction of the whole or part without the publishers' written permission is prohibited.

Key Grammar Workbook Starter Level
ISBN: 978 0602 20679 6
Starter Level Easy Order Pack: 978 0602 20621 5
Starter Level Workbook 6 Pack: 978 0602 20643 7

First published 2005

20 19 18 17 16
15 14

Cover illustration by Pet Gotohda
Cover design by Tom Cole
Designed by Nicki Wise, Te Marama Design
Illustrations by Andrea Pretrlik Huseinovic, Maddy McClellan, Christina Bretschneider

Printed and bound by Malaysia (CTP-VVP)

Grammar Starter Level Workbook

Contents

Unit 1	Sentence construction 1	page 2
Unit 2	Sentence construction 2	page 4
Unit 3	Sentence construction 3	page 5
Unit 4	Using full stops	page 6
Unit 5	Capital letters	page 8
Unit 6	Word order in sentences	page 10
Unit 7	Uses of capital letters	page 12
Unit 8	Linking words	page 14
Unit 9	Organisational devices	page 15
Unit 10	Question marks	page 16
Unit 12	Exclamation marks	page 18
Unit 13	Commas	page 19
Unit 14	Speech marks	page 20
Unit 15	Speech bubbles	page 22
Unit 16	Ways of presenting text	page 23
Unit 18	Commas in lists	page 24
Unit 19	Regular past tense	page 26
Unit 20	Tricky past tenses!	page 28
Unit 21	Does my sentence make sense?	page 30
Unit 22	Question words	page 32

Unit 1 Sentence construction 1

🔑 Key idea

A verb is a "doing" or a "being" word. All sentences need a verb to say what is happening.

Who's doing what?

Look at each of these pictures and write the verb which shows what the person is doing in each one. Choose the verbs from the box. *(1 mark for each correct answer)*

singing	running	fishing	swimming	drinking
cooking	crying	writing	eating	kicking

1.
2.
3.
4.
5.
6.
7.
8.
9.
10.

Finish the sentence

Choose a verb to complete each sentence.
(1 mark for each correct answer)

| swam   drove   ran |
| danced   watched |
| barked   washed |
| played   drilled   changed |

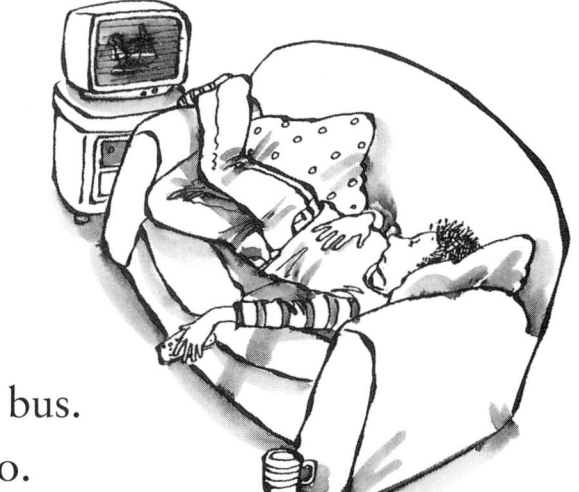

1 The lady _____ for the bus.
2 Tariq _____ at the disco.
3 Tariq _____ T.V. after school.
4 The dog _____ at the old man.
5 Tariq _____ his hands.
6 The magician _____ a bird into a rabbit!
7 The dentist _____ Tariq's tooth.
8 Tariq and Adam _____ football in the park.
9 Adam _____ in the pool.
10 Tariq's dad _____ to school in his new car.

Spot the verb!

Some of these sentences have a verb missing! Try to spot them, putting a tick or a cross after each sentence. Tick if the verb is there or put a cross if the verb is missing. *(1 mark for each correct answer)*

1 Tariq shut the door.
2 Mary the car.
3 Amy the park.
4 I saw a bird.
5 The boy seven.
6 Jill watched the film.
7 Tariq cut the string.
8 He the new cards.
9 The cup is red.
10 Tariq read two books.

unit 2 Sentence construction 2

Key idea

A sentence is a group of words which carries a meaning.
Sentences must make sense.

    Amy walked to school.

This sentence tells us how Amy got to school. It makes sense and is a complete idea.

Correct it!

These sentences have got mixed up. Underline the wrong word and write the correct one at the end of the sentence. *(3 marks for each correct answer)*

1 The cat was barking. _____
2 The bear was very tiny. _____
3 An ant is big and furry. _____
4 The dog drank the milk. _____
5 A rabbit lives in a swamp. _____
6 A crocodile lives in a hutch. _____

Get it right!

These sentences do not make sense. Change the word in bold so that the sentence makes sense. *(2 marks for each correct answer)*

1 Amy **are** a very nice girl. _____
2 Tariq **have** a cat. _____
3 The dogs **has** long tails. _____
4 Dad **like** ice cream. _____
5 The **shoe** were too tight. _____
6 I think Adam **are** a very kind boy. _____

unit 3
Sentence construction 3

Key idea

Sentences have a subject and an object.
Sentences must be clear and make sense.
The subject tells us 'who' or 'what' the sentence is about. The subject goes with the verb. The object of a sentence is the person or thing the subject is doing something to.

Who's doing what?

The subject of these sentences is missing.
Write in the subject for each one. Use the words in the box to help you. *(3 marks for each correct answer)*

1 The _____ sat in his kennel.
2 The _____ played with her kittens.
3 The _____ read a story in Assembly.
4 The _____ ate a carrot.
5 A _____ flew onto the tree.

| dog teacher |
| rabbit |
| cat bird |

Finish the sentence

The object in each of these sentences is missing. Write in the object for each one. Use the words in the box to help you.

(3 marks for each correct answer)

1 The boy batted the _____.
2 The postman dropped a _____.
3 The dog found a long, white _____.
4 The cow chewed the _____.
5 The bird sat on the _____.

| letter bone |
| ball grass |
| branch |

Unit 4 Using full stops

🔑 Key idea

A full stop marks the end of a sentence. It shows the reader where one idea ends.

Amy wanted a new book. She went to the shops to buy one.

Two full stops are used, as there are two ideas, each in their own sentence.

Spot the stop!

Look at these sentences. The full stop is in the wrong place. Cross it out and put it in the right place. *(1 mark for each correct answer)*

1 Adam. went to the shops
2 Amy saw. her sister
3 The man walked. into town
4 Tariq played with his friend. Sam
5 The lady had two. bags of shopping
6 Adam helped in the. garden
7 The. cow was in the field.
8 Amy flew her. kite on Saturday
9 John saw the. fireworks
10 The lady sang a beautiful. song

Find the sentence

Some words have been added to the ends of these sentences. Put in the full stop to show where the sentence should end and cross out the extra words! *(1 mark for each correct answer)*

For example: John was happy. ~~doors shops~~

1 Tariq enjoyed his party. ~~waits says~~
2 Amy watched the film. ~~snow open~~
3 The doctor went to see Adam. ~~shake David Hamid~~
4 The shops were very busy. ~~time cooking frosty~~
5 John went fishing with his dad. ~~baby shoes Tuesday~~
6 Amy saw a magic show. ~~ties paper poster~~
7 The King spoke to the crowd. ~~strange book cows~~
8 Yesterday Tariq built a model. ~~glass coats~~
9 The owl hooted in the night. ~~cards~~
10 It was a very hot day. ~~windows newspaper~~

Correct the story

There are ten missing full stops in this short story. Put in the full stops so that the story makes sense. *(1 mark for each correct answer)*

Amy was reading in her bedroom Her mum came in and asked her if she wanted to go to the fair Amy was so excited Later that afternoon Amy and her mum set off When they got there Amy saw the dodgems Amy wanted to have a go Her mum agreed and she had two rides Then Amy saw the ghost train Amy was a bit scared but she had a ride It was lots of fun

Unit 5: Capital letters

🔑 Key idea

Capital letters are used to show the start of a sentence and to identify proper nouns, such as names of people.

Everyone saw the clowns and Freddy was the biggest clown of all.

Everyone starts with a capital letter as it begins the sentence. **Freddy** begins with a capital letter as it is a name.

Send in the clowns!

Write out the names of the clowns. Each name should start with a capital letter. *(1 mark for each correct answer)*

| coco | daisy | billy | sidney | freddy |
| joey | archie | peggy | winston | smartie |

_____   _____

_____   _____

_____   _____

_____   _____

_____   _____

A capital idea!

Write out each sentence remembering to start with a capital letter.

(1 mark for each correct answer)

1. the tent was very big. _____
2. joey had orange hair. _____
3. the tickets cost £3.50. _____
4. a lady was selling ice creams. _____
5. the clowns made us laugh. _____
6. i laughed at the clowns. _____
7. freddy fell off his chair! _____
8. mum got me a clown badge. _____
9. it was an exciting show. _____
10. i would like to see it again. _____

What happened next?

Write out five sentences about some funny things the clowns might have done. Remember to start each one with a capital letter. Use these words to help you: clown, mess, threw, pies, water, car, squirted and crash. *(2 marks for each correct sentence)*

_____

_____

_____

_____

_____

Unit 6 Word order in sentences

Key idea

Each sentence has a subject and an object. Words in a sentence must be in the correct order to make sense.

An alien flew down to Earth.

This sentence makes sense. The words are in the correct order. The sentence tells us something. It conveys an idea.

Alien message

Translate this alien message by putting the words into the correct order in each sentence. *(2 marks for each correct sentence)*

Venus from we send greetings. Peace we come in. friends your are we. Chocolate like we. Large is our very spaceship.

_____

_____

_____

Alien objects

Complete this message from the aliens by putting in an object for each sentence. *(1 mark for each correct answer)*

We have read all your _____

We have tasted your _____

Our spaceship landed on the _____

We write with long _____

We would like to eat some _____

Our planet crashed into _____

We have looked at your _____

Our computer has tested your _____

We are excited by your _____

Our troops have been into the _____

Write to the aliens!

Make up your own message for the aliens. You will need to write out five short sentences, changing the word order so that it does not make sense to humans. Make sure you include all the words you will need in each sentence. Make sure each sentence has a subject. *(2 marks for each correct sentence)*

For example:

Where have you come from? = Come from have where you?

_____

_____

_____

_____

Unit 7 Capital letters

Key idea

Capital letters are used to show the start of a sentence, and to identify proper nouns – names of people, places, titles and times.

Capitalise!

Write these words below, so that each one starts with a capital letter. *(1 mark for each correct answer)*

may _____   rome _____

i _____   fred _____

paul _____   tuesday _____

february _____   sally _____

sunday _____   august _____

Choose a word!

Write eight words that need to start with a capital letter. You might choose the names of people, places, days or months of the year. *(1 mark for each correct answer)*

_____   _____

_____   _____

_____   _____

_____   _____

Now write the name of your favourite book or story. *(2 marks)*

_____

Which is right?

Adam has got mixed up and written every word below with a capital letter! Copy it out correctly, keeping only the correct capitals. *(0.5 mark for each correction)*

On Sunday I Saw My Friend Sam. He Has A Dog Called Scruffy. We Took Scruffy To The Park On Sunshine Street. It Was Lots Of Fun! We Will Go Again Next Sunday.

_____

_____

_____

_____

Unit 8 Linking words

Key idea

We can join short sentences together to make longer, more interesting sentences. We use link words like AND, SO or BUT.

The lion was hungry. The lion ate some meat.
= The lion was hungry so he ate some meat.

We do not need the second "The lion" as we know he is the subject of the sentence.

Zoo report

Amy wrote a report of her trip to the zoo. Join these pairs of sentences together using "and". *(3 marks for each correct sentence)*

1 I put on my coat. I went to the zoo. _____
2 I carried my camera. I took photos. _____
3 I saw the zebras. I saw the chimps. _____
4 I fed the rabbits. I fed the ducks. _____
5 The chimps were noisy. They were funny. _____

All mixed up!

Choose from "and", "so", "because" or "but" to join these sentences. *(3 marks for each correct sentence)*

1 I am going home. It is too late to go to the zoo. _____
2 You are helping me. She is not. _____
3 I love the chimps. They are funny animals. _____
4 I ate an ice cream. I ate a hot dog. _____
5 I wanted to buy a T-shirt. I didn't have enough money. _____

Unit 9 Organisational devices

🔑 Key idea

We use short sentences, letters, numbers or bullet points and pictures to set out instructions.

Set it out!

Write out these instructions so that they are easy to follow.
(15 marks)

Giving your puppy a bath. First, fill the bath half way with warm water. Put your puppy in the bath and wash it with soap and water. Rinse the puppy carefully. Lift your puppy out of the bath. Dry your puppy with a towel and brush its coat.

_____   _____

_____   _____

_____   _____

Make a snowman

These instructions are mixed up. Read them carefully and put a letter from "a" to "f" next to each one to order them. *(15 marks)*

a. Firstly, roll a large ball of snow.
___ Finally, put a hat on his head and a scarf around his neck.
___ Roll a smaller ball and put it on top for a head.
___ Push in two sticks for arms and put gloves on for hands.
___ Add two stones and a carrot to the smaller ball for a face.

Unit 10 Question marks

Key idea

A question mark is used to show a question.
It comes at the end of the question.
You do not need a full stop after a question mark.

>What is your name?

>How old are you?

These are both questions, as they need an answer.

Here we go!

**Add question marks to the end of these five questions.
Make sure you form the question mark carefully.** *(1 mark for each correct answer)*

1. Is it a long trip
2. Are you going by plane
3. Do you have two bags
4. Will the plane land in Glasgow
5. Is this a jumbo jet

Find that question!

Look through one of your reading books and write down five questions that you find in the story. Remember to begin each with a capital letter and put a question mark at the end.
(10 marks)

_____

_____

_____

_____

_____

Interview a pilot!

Here are five answers a pilot gave, but what were the questions? Look at the answers and write the question you think he was asked. *(3 marks for each correct question)*

_____

I have been a pilot for 4 years.

_____

My favourite airport is in Paris.

_____

Yes, I do like my uniform.

_____

I wanted to be a pilot when I was young.

_____

I was born in Manchester.

Unit 12 Exclamation marks

Key idea

We use exclamation marks to show that something scary, exciting or surprising has happened. They are also used to show that someone in a story is shouting or something is loud.

Read the signs!

These signs have their exclamation marks missing. Copy them carefully and add the exclamation marks. *(2 marks for each one)*

DANGER _____

Falling Rocks _____

Do not swim here _____

Private _____

Do not enter _____

The spooky castle

There are ten exclamation marks missing from this short story. Read it carefully and put them in. *(1 mark for each correct answer)*

Aneena went into the old, spooky castle. CRASH. The old clock fell off the wall all by itself. Aneena thought it must be a ghost. THUD. The door slammed shut by itself. BOOM. WHOOSH. A cannon on the roof went off. Aneena was very scared, so she pulled the door but it was stuck.

Finish the story!

Write out the end of Aneena's story. *(10 marks)*

Commas

🔑 Key idea

Commas are used to add extra information or to create a pause. They break up longer sentences into smaller parts.

Quickly, Davina locked the door!

Exciting sentences!

Complete these sentences in an exciting way, by finishing each sentence after the comma. *(3 marks for each correct sentence)*

Suddenly, _____

Just at that moment, _____

All at once, _____

The door slowly opened, _____

Although it was dark, _____

Finally, _____

Commas in pairs!

Place the commas where you think extra information has been added to each sentence. *(2 marks for each correct sentence)*

The clock which was very old did not work.

Davina who was wearing a red dress hid behind the red curtains.

The rain which had been pouring all day finally stopped.

Davina in her loudest voice shouted from behind the curtains!

Everyone including Davina's mum was very surprised!

Everyone including Davina had to walk home through the rain.

unit 14 Speech marks

Key idea

We use speech marks to show when someone is speaking.

"Are you Fred the Robot?" asked the Captain.

What the Captain said is put inside speech marks.

What did you say?

Write some speech for each of these characters inside the speech marks. Remember question marks or exclamation marks go INSIDE the speech marks. *(2 marks for each correct sentence)*

"_____" asked the teacher.

"_____," called Mum.

"_____" shouted the policeman.

"_____" laughed the clown.

"_____" asked the shopkeeper.

Who said that?

It is important if we're writing a story with more than one character in it to say who is speaking. Read these lines of speech and write down who might have said them. *(1 mark for each correct answer)*

"It's time you did your homework!" called _____

"It's time for Assembly," said _____

"Hand over your money!" shouted _____

"I'll turn you into a frog!" cackled _____

"Can I help you, Sir?" asked _____

"You've got a broken arm," said _____

Where do they go?

The speech marks in this story are in the wrong place. Cross them out and put them in the right places. *(1 mark for each correct answer)*

Can I help you? "said the lady at the counter". Yes, "please," replied Carl. "He wanted to buy" a new bike. How much is that one? he asked. "It's £100, replied the lady." Oh dear, said "Carl", I'll have to save up my "pocket money!" Carl left the shop, but he would "get that bike, one day."

Speech bubbles

🔑 Key idea

A speech bubble is used to show who is speaking and what they have said. Speech bubbles are used in pictures, cartoons, posters and information texts. We do not use speech marks inside a speech bubble.

Perfect pets!

Write what each pet is saying in the correct speech bubble.

(5 marks for each correct answer)

"I'll fetch that stick!"   "I've laid you an egg!"   "Can I have some milk?"

Look after your pets!

Here is Jaswinder, the vet. Write in her tips for looking after your pet. There are some clues to help you in the pictures.

(15 marks)

Unit 16: Ways of presenting texts – BLOCK CAPITALS

Key idea

We use BLOCK CAPITALS when writing to show that something is important, scary, exciting or dangerous.
They also mark someone is shouting or giving an instruction or a warning.

STOP!   "Don't go in THERE!"

A capital idea

Write out the alphabet in BLOCK CAPITALS.
Make sure each letter is formed correctly! *(0.5 mark for each correct letter and 1 mark for the correct order)*

___ ___ ___ ___ ___ ___

___ ___ ___ ___ ___ ___

___ ___ ___ ___ ___ ___

___ ___ ___ ___ ___ ___

___ ___

The right sign

Write out these signs using BLOCK CAPITALS. Then write five more of your own. *(2 marks for each correct sign)*

Beware of the dog.   _____

_____   _____

High Tides.   _____

_____   _____

Open.   _____

_____   _____

Commas in lists

Key idea

Commas are used to separate items in a list.

   Joe put a pencil, a rubber, a sharpener and an apple into his bag.

The last two items in a list are joined by "and" to show it is the end of this list.

Comma collections

Put the missing commas into these lists. *(1 mark for each correct comma)*

Apple orange grape and pear.
Tea coffee milk and water.
Pencil felt-tip crayon and pen.
Card envelope letter and stamp.
Plate saucer jug and cup.

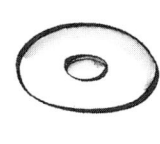

What is missing?

Write out these lists, putting in the missing commas. Remember to place an "and" between the last two items. *(1 mark for each correct comma and "and")*

Drum guitar piano recorder.

Hammer saw nail screw.

Oak ash elm willow pine.

What do you like?

Finish these lists. *(2 marks for each list)*

I like to drink _____ _____ and _____.

I don't like _____ _____ ___ _____.

I like to play _____ _____ ___ _____.

I wish I had a _____ _____ ___ _____.

I would like to go to _____ _____ ___ _____.

Unit 19: Regular past tense

Key idea

We use the past tense to say when something has already happened. Many verbs make the past tense by adding **ed**.

I wash my face – it is happening now; it is the PRESENT TENSE.

I wash**ed** my face – it happened some time ago; it is the PAST TENSE.

Back in time!

Write out these verbs turning them into the past tense by adding ed. *(1 mark for each correct answer)*

pull	_____	jump	_____
play	_____	push	_____
look	_____	call	_____
shout	_____	brush	_____
watch	_____	turn	_____

Drop the 'e' and add 'ed'

Make these verbs into the past tense by dropping the e and adding ed. *(0.5 mark for each correct answer)*

race	_____	skate	_____
cuddle	_____	change	_____
smile	_____	wipe	_____
wiggle	_____	hope	_____

Time for a story

Change the verbs so this story is in the past tense. *(1 mark for each correct past tense and 1 for each sentence written out correctly)*

Last Tuesday, Sophie and I play our favourite game, Tug of War. I pull very hard. I watch the rope carefully. I move my feet slowly. I call to the winner. I enjoy this game!

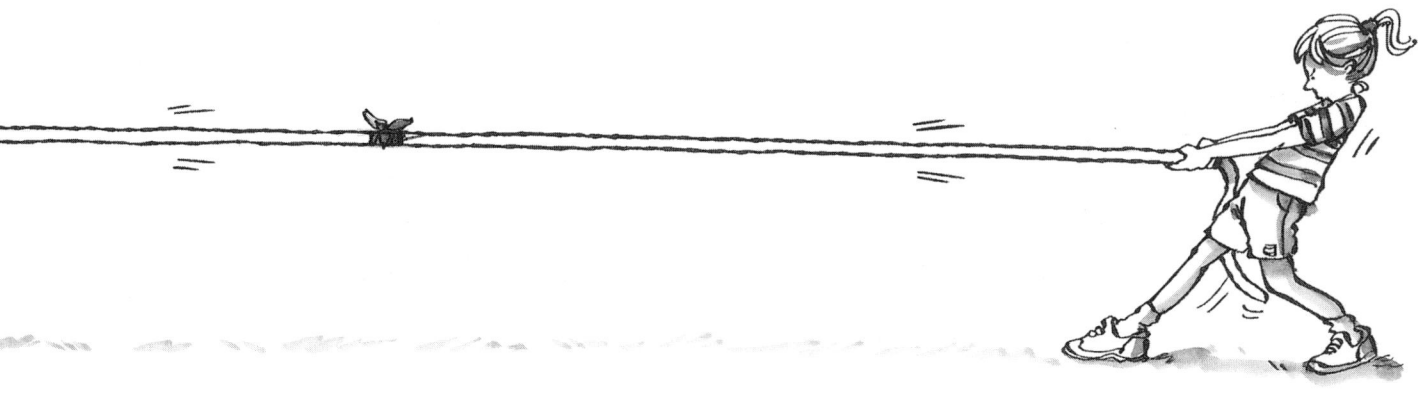

unit 20 — Tricky past tenses

 **Key idea**

Not all verbs add **ed** to put them into the past. Verbs which do not are called **irregular** verbs.

I make a model = I made a model.

We can check by adding **ed**. If it doesn't sound right, then it must be an irregular verb.

All in the past!

Write these past tenses in the present tense. *(1 mark for each correct answer)*

For example, saw = see

went = _____
took = _____
drove = _____
came = _____
ate   = _____
fought = _____
grew = _____
won   = _____
slept = _____
hid   = _____

28

Verb detective!

Underline the verbs which do not use ed to make the past tense. Check by saying each verb with ed at the end. *(0.5 mark for each correct answer)*

> play see make fly wish run call give sit
> drink turn eat write catch jump dig tell
> paint build munch ride pick hold go
> chase sing have shout ring wear

All mixed up!

Rewrite this story, so that it uses the correct past tense.
(2 marks for each correct tense)

Yesterday Amit **go** to the seaside. He **takes** his swimming kit and he **swimmed** in the sea. He **eat** an ice cream and **writed** a postcard to his friend.

_____

_____

_____

_____

_____

_____

_____

Unit 21 — Does my sentence make sense?

Key idea

Sentences must make sense and all their parts must work together.

The Princess wore his tiara = The Princess wore her tiara.

This sentence doesn't make sense as the "Princess" is wearing "his" tiara. Each part of the sentence must "agree".

We must also check that the subject and the verb "agree". The King were sad = The King was sad.

Get it right!

Choose the correct word to finish each sentence. *(1 mark for each correct answer)*

1 The King wore _____ crown. (his/her)
2 The Queen wore _____ jewels. (his/her)
3 The people _____ happy. (was/were)
4 The castle _____ very big. (is/are)
5 There _____ lots of flowers in the garden. (was/were)

Is this correct?

Underline the word that is wrong. Put the correct word in the space. *(2 marks for each correct sentence)*

1 The Prince were tired. _____
2 The boys was friends. _____
3 The King like to eat sweets. _____
4 The Queen give the Prince a pet. _____
5 It are a kitten. _____

The prince's cat

Correct the Prince's mistakes in his pet report. Check that each sentence makes sense! *(3 marks for each correct answer)*

My cat like to chase mice. It have very soft fur. There is lots of rats in the castle and my cat chases it! I think my cat are wonderful.

Unit 22 Question words

🔑 Key idea

When we write a question we often start with a question word.
A question word asks a question all by itself.
Who? Why? When? Where? What? How? These are all question words.
We always put a question mark at the end of a question.

Who or how?

Put in the correct question word to finish these questions.

(2 marks for each correct sentence)

1 _____ did you get here?
2 _____ told you that?
3 _____ old are you?
4 _____ did you do that?
5 _____ is your favourite footballer?

Interview time!

Write out a series of questions that you would like to ask a friend, your teacher or a member of your family. Use the question words given to start off each question. Make sure each one ends with a question mark. *(20 marks)*

How _____

Where _____

When _____

Who _____

What _____

Key Grammar is a brand new resource, specifically planned to cover all the key grammar objectives in self-contained units of work. The pupil books feature:

- clear, progressive units covering all key learning objectives
- plenty of practice and consolidation work
- opportunities to challenge and extend children's learning
- a clear mark scheme
- exercises in an appropriate context, with engaging illustrations

The workbooks provide activities for additional practice, differentiation, and homework. The important language skills coverage in **Key Grammar** is complemented by two associated series: **Key Comprehension** and **Key Spelling** – up-to-date and engaging resources which reinforce key teaching points and enable children to practise, consolidate and extend their learning. For further information about **Key Comprehension** and **Key Spelling** call our Customer Services Department on **(+44) (0)1865 888000**.

ISBN 978-0-602206-79-6

Author: Chris Wardle

Ginn
Halley Court, Jordan Hill, Oxford OX2 8EJ
a division of Harcourt Education Limited

www.myprimary.co.uk
Help and support for teachers plus the widest range of education solutions

Ginn is a registered trademark of Harcourt Education Limited

© Harcourt Education Limited 2005

This book is copyright and reproduction of the whole or part without the publishers' written permission is prohibited.

Key Grammar Workbook Starter Level
ISBN: 978 0602 20679 6
Starter Level Easy Order Pack: 978 0602 20621 5
Starter Level Workbook 6 Pack: 978 0602 20643 7

First published 2005

20 19 18 17 16
15 14

Cover illustration by Pet Gotohda
Cover design by Tom Cole
Designed by Nicki Wise, Te Marama Design
Illustrations by Andrea Pretrlik Huseinovic, Maddy McClellan, Christina Bretschneider

Printed and bound by Malaysia (CTP-VVP)

Grammar Starter Level Workbook

Contents

Unit 1	Sentence construction 1	page 2
Unit 2	Sentence construction 2	page 4
Unit 3	Sentence construction 3	page 5
Unit 4	Using full stops	page 6
Unit 5	Capital letters	page 8
Unit 6	Word order in sentences	page 10
Unit 7	Uses of capital letters	page 12
Unit 8	Linking words	page 14
Unit 9	Organisational devices	page 15
Unit 10	Question marks	page 16
Unit 12	Exclamation marks	page 18
Unit 13	Commas	page 19
Unit 14	Speech marks	page 20
Unit 15	Speech bubbles	page 22
Unit 16	Ways of presenting text	page 23
Unit 18	Commas in lists	page 24
Unit 19	Regular past tense	page 26
Unit 20	Tricky past tenses!	page 28
Unit 21	Does my sentence make sense?	page 30
Unit 22	Question words	page 32

Unit 1

Sentence construction 1

🔑 Key idea

A verb is a "doing" or a "being" word. All sentences need a verb to say what is happening.

Who's doing what?

Look at each of these pictures and write the verb which shows what the person is doing in each one. Choose the verbs from the box. *(1 mark for each correct answer)*

| singing | running | fishing | swimming | drinking |
| cooking | crying | writing | eating | kicking |

1
2
3
4
5
6
7
8
9
10

Finish the sentence

Choose a verb to complete each sentence.
(1 mark for each correct answer)

| swam   drove   ran |
| danced   watched |
| barked   washed |
| played   drilled   changed |

1 The lady _____ for the bus.
2 Tariq _____ at the disco.
3 Tariq _____ T.V. after school.
4 The dog _____ at the old man.
5 Tariq _____ his hands.
6 The magician _____ a bird into a rabbit!
7 The dentist _____ Tariq's tooth.
8 Tariq and Adam _____ football in the park.
9 Adam _____ in the pool.
10 Tariq's dad _____ to school in his new car.

Spot the verb!

Some of these sentences have a verb missing! Try to spot them, putting a tick or a cross after each sentence. Tick if the verb is there or put a cross if the verb is missing. *(1 mark for each correct answer)*

1 Tariq shut the door.   6 Jill watched the film.
2 Mary the car.   7 Tariq cut the string.
3 Amy the park.   8 He the new cards.
4 I saw a bird.   9 The cup is red.
5 The boy seven.   10 Tariq read two books.

Sentence construction 2

Key idea

A sentence is a group of words which carries a meaning.
Sentences must make sense.

     Amy walked to school.

This sentence tells us how Amy got to school. It makes sense and is a complete idea.

Correct it!

These sentences have got mixed up. Underline the wrong word and write the correct one at the end of the sentence. *(3 marks for each correct answer)*

1 The cat was barking. _____
2 The bear was very tiny. _____
3 An ant is big and furry. _____
4 The dog drank the milk. _____
5 A rabbit lives in a swamp. _____
6 A crocodile lives in a hutch. _____

Get it right!

These sentences do not make sense. Change the word in bold so that the sentence makes sense. *(2 marks for each correct answer)*

1 Amy **are** a very nice girl. _____

2 Tariq **have** a cat. _____

3 The dogs **has** long tails. _____

4 Dad **like** ice cream. _____

5 The **shoe** were too tight. _____

6 I think Adam **are** a very kind boy. _____

Unit 3 Sentence construction 3

Key idea

Sentences have a subject and an object.
Sentences must be clear and make sense.
The subject tells us 'who' or 'what' the sentence is about. The subject goes with the verb. The object of a sentence is the person or thing the subject is doing something to.

Who's doing what?

The subject of these sentences is missing.
Write in the subject for each one. Use the words in the box to help you. *(3 marks for each correct answer)*

1 The _____ sat in his kennel.
2 The _____ played with her kittens.
3 The _____ read a story in Assembly.
4 The _____ ate a carrot.
5 A _____ flew onto the tree.

> dog teacher
> rabbit
> cat bird

Finish the sentence

The object in each of these sentences is missing. Write in the object for each one. Use the words in the box to help you.

(3 marks for each correct answer)

1 The boy batted the _____.
2 The postman dropped a _____.
3 The dog found a long, white _____.
4 The cow chewed the _____.
5 The bird sat on the _____.

> letter bone
> ball grass
> branch

Unit 4 Using full stops

🔑 Key idea

A full stop marks the end of a sentence. It shows the reader where one idea ends.

Amy wanted a new book. She went to the shops to buy one.

Two full stops are used, as there are two ideas, each in their own sentence.

Spot the stop!

Look at these sentences. The full stop is in the wrong place. Cross it out and put it in the right place. *(1 mark for each correct answer)*

1 Adam. went to the shops
2 Amy saw. her sister
3 The man walked. into town
4 Tariq played with his friend. Sam
5 The lady had two. bags of shopping
6 Adam helped in the. garden
7 The. cow was in the field.
8 Amy flew her. kite on Saturday
9 John saw the. fireworks
10 The lady sang a beautiful. song

Find the sentence

Some words have been added to the ends of these sentences. Put in the full stop to show where the sentence should end and cross out the extra words! *(1 mark for each correct answer)*

For example: John was happy. ~~doors shops~~

1 Tariq enjoyed his party waits says
2 Amy watched the film snow open
3 The doctor went to see Adam shake David Hamid
4 The shops were very busy time cooking frosty
5 John went fishing with his dad baby shoes Tuesday
6 Amy saw a magic show ties paper poster
7 The King spoke to the crowd strange book cows
8 Yesterday Tariq built a model glass coats
9 The owl hooted in the night cards
10 It was a very hot day windows newspaper

Correct the story

There are ten missing full stops in this short story. Put in the full stops so that the story makes sense. *(1 mark for each correct answer)*

Amy was reading in her bedroom Her mum came in and asked her if she wanted to go to the fair Amy was so excited Later that afternoon Amy and her mum set off When they got there Amy saw the dodgems Amy wanted to have a go Her mum agreed and she had two rides Then Amy saw the ghost train Amy was a bit scared but she had a ride It was lots of fun

Unit 5: Capital letters

🔑 Key idea

Capital letters are used to show the start of a sentence and to identify proper nouns, such as names of people.

Everyone saw the clowns and Freddy was the biggest clown of all. **Everyone** starts with a capital letter as it begins the sentence. **Freddy** begins with a capital letter as it is a name.

Send in the clowns!

Write out the names of the clowns. Each name should start with a capital letter. *(1 mark for each correct answer)*

| coco | daisy | billy | sidney | freddy |
| joey | archie | peggy | winston | smartie |

_____   _____

_____   _____

_____   _____

_____   _____

_____   _____

A capital idea!

Write out each sentence remembering to start with a capital letter.

(1 mark for each correct answer)

1. the tent was very big. _____
2. joey had orange hair. _____
3. the tickets cost £3.50. _____
4. a lady was selling ice creams. _____
5. the clowns made us laugh. _____
6. i laughed at the clowns. _____
7. freddy fell off his chair! _____
8. mum got me a clown badge. _____
9. it was an exciting show. _____
10. i would like to see it again. _____

What happened next?

Write out five sentences about some funny things the clowns might have done. Remember to start each one with a capital letter. Use these words to help you: clown, mess, threw, pies, water, car, squirted and crash. *(2 marks for each correct sentence)*

_____

_____

_____

_____

_____

Unit 6 Word order in sentences

Key idea

Each sentence has a subject and an object. Words in a sentence must be in the correct order to make sense.

An alien flew down to Earth.

This sentence makes sense. The words are in the correct order. The sentence tells us something. It conveys an idea.

Alien message

Translate this alien message by putting the words into the correct order in each sentence. *(2 marks for each correct sentence)*

Venus from we send greetings. Peace we come in. friends your are we. Chocolate like we. Large is our very spaceship.

_____

_____

_____

Alien objects

Complete this message from the aliens by putting in an object for each sentence. *(1 mark for each correct answer)*

We have read all your _____

We have tasted your _____

Our spaceship landed on the _____

We write with long _____

We would like to eat some _____

Our planet crashed into _____

We have looked at your _____

Our computer has tested your _____

We are excited by your _____

Our troops have been into the _____

Write to the aliens!

Make up your own message for the aliens. You will need to write out five short sentences, changing the word order so that it does not make sense to humans. Make sure you include all the words you will need in each sentence. Make sure each sentence has a subject. *(2 marks for each correct sentence)*

For example:

Where have you come from? = Come from have where you?

_____

_____

_____

_____

Unit 7 Capital letters

🔑 Key idea

Capital letters are used to show the start of a sentence, and to identify proper nouns – names of people, places, titles and times.

Capitalise!

Write these words below, so that each one starts with a capital letter. *(1 mark for each correct answer)*

may _____   rome _____

i _____   fred _____

paul _____   tuesday _____

february _____   sally _____

sunday _____   august _____

Choose a word!

Write eight words that need to start with a capital letter. You might choose the names of people, places, days or months of the year. *(1 mark for each correct answer)*

_____   _____

_____   _____

_____   _____

_____   _____

Now write the name of your favourite book or story. *(2 marks)*

_____

Which is right?

Adam has got mixed up and written every word below with a capital letter! Copy it out correctly, keeping only the correct capitals. *(0.5 mark for each correction)*

On Sunday I Saw My Friend Sam. He Has A Dog Called Scruffy. We Took Scruffy To The Park On Sunshine Street. It Was Lots Of Fun! We Will Go Again Next Sunday.

_____

_____

_____

_____

Linking words

Key idea

We can join short sentences together to make longer, more interesting sentences. We use link words like AND, SO or BUT.

The lion was hungry. The lion ate some meat.
= The lion was hungry so he ate some meat.

We do not need the second "The lion" as we know he is the subject of the sentence.

Zoo report

Amy wrote a report of her trip to the zoo. Join these pairs of sentences together using "and". *(3 marks for each correct sentence)*

1 I put on my coat. I went to the zoo. _____
2 I carried my camera. I took photos. _____
3 I saw the zebras. I saw the chimps. _____
4 I fed the rabbits. I fed the ducks. _____
5 The chimps were noisy. They were funny. _____

All mixed up!

Choose from "and", "so", "because" or "but" to join these sentences. *(3 marks for each correct sentence)*

1 I am going home. It is too late to go to the zoo. _____
2 You are helping me. She is not. _____
3 I love the chimps. They are funny animals. _____
4 I ate an ice cream. I ate a hot dog. _____
5 I wanted to buy a T-shirt. I didn't have enough money. _____

Unit 9 Organisational devices

🔑 Key idea

We use short sentences, letters, numbers or bullet points and pictures to set out instructions.

Set it out!

Write out these instructions so that they are easy to follow.
(15 marks)

Giving your puppy a bath. First, fill the bath half way with warm water. Put your puppy in the bath and wash it with soap and water. Rinse the puppy carefully. Lift your puppy out of the bath. Dry your puppy with a towel and brush its coat.

_____   _____

_____   _____

_____   _____

Make a snowman

These instructions are mixed up. Read them carefully and put a letter from "a" to "f" next to each one to order them. *(15 marks)*

a. Firstly, roll a large ball of snow.
___ Finally, put a hat on his head and a scarf around his neck.
___ Roll a smaller ball and put it on top for a head.
___ Push in two sticks for arms and put gloves on for hands.
___ Add two stones and a carrot to the smaller ball for a face.

Unit 10 Question marks

Key idea

A question mark is used to show a question.
It comes at the end of the question.
You do not need a full stop after a question mark.

>What is your name?
>
>How old are you?

These are both questions, as they need an answer.

Here we go!

Add question marks to the end of these five questions. Make sure you form the question mark carefully. *(1 mark for each correct answer)*

1. Is it a long trip
2. Are you going by plane
3. Do you have two bags
4. Will the plane land in Glasgow
5. Is this a jumbo jet

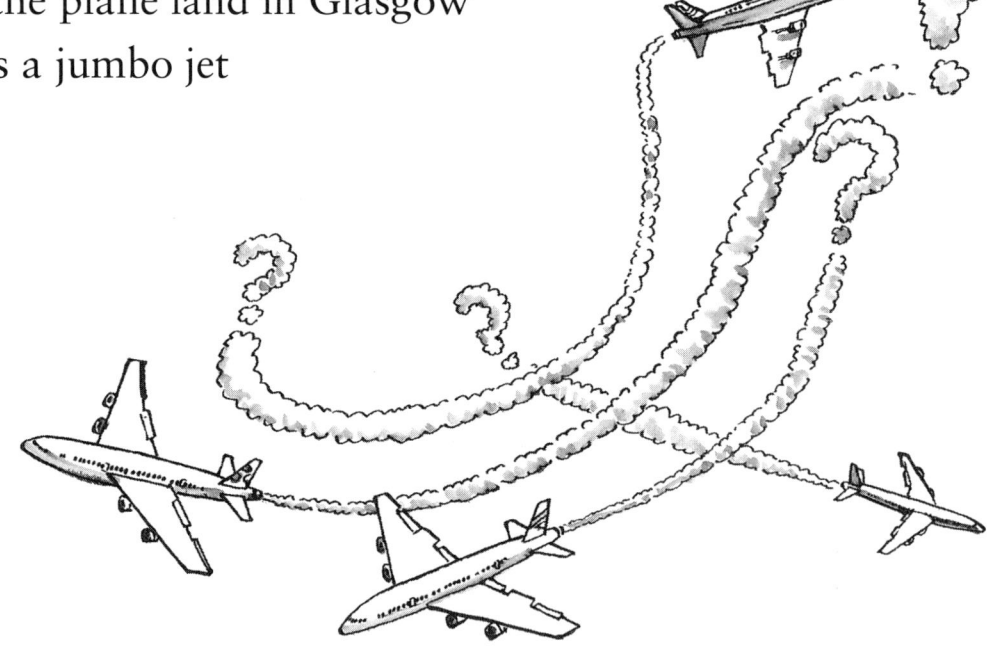

Find that question!

Look through one of your reading books and write down five questions that you find in the story. Remember to begin each with a capital letter and put a question mark at the end.
(10 marks)

_____

_____

_____

_____

_____

Interview a pilot!

Here are five answers a pilot gave, but what were the questions? Look at the answers and write the question you think he was asked. *(3 marks for each correct question)*

_____

I have been a pilot for 4 years.

_____

My favourite airport is in Paris.

_____

Yes, I do like my uniform.

_____

I wanted to be a pilot when I was young.

_____

I was born in Manchester.

Unit 12: Exclamation marks

🔑 Key idea

We use exclamation marks to show that something scary, exciting or surprising has happened. They are also used to show that someone in a story is shouting or something is loud.

Read the signs!

These signs have their exclamation marks missing. Copy them carefully and add the exclamation marks. *(2 marks for each one)*

DANGER
Falling Rocks
Do not swim here
Private
Do not enter

The spooky castle

There are ten exclamation marks missing from this short story. Read it carefully and put them in. *(1 mark for each correct answer)*

Aneena went into the old, spooky castle. CRASH. The old clock fell off the wall all by itself. Aneena thought it must be a ghost. THUD. The door slammed shut by itself. BOOM. WHOOSH. A cannon on the roof went off. Aneena was very scared, so she pulled the door but it was stuck.

Finish the story!

Write out the end of Aneena's story. *(10 marks)*

Commas

🔑 Key idea

Commas are used to add extra information or to create a pause. They break up longer sentences into smaller parts.

Quickly, Davina locked the door!

Exciting sentences!

Complete these sentences in an exciting way, by finishing each sentence after the comma. *(3 marks for each correct sentence)*

Suddenly, _____

Just at that moment, _____

All at once, _____

The door slowly opened, _____

Although it was dark, _____

Finally, _____

Commas in pairs!

Place the commas where you think extra information has been added to each sentence. *(2 marks for each correct sentence)*

The clock which was very old did not work.

Davina who was wearing a red dress hid behind the red curtains.

The rain which had been pouring all day finally stopped.

Davina in her loudest voice shouted from behind the curtains!

Everyone including Davina's mum was very surprised!

Everyone including Davina had to walk home through the rain.

Unit 14 Speech marks

Key idea

We use speech marks to show when someone is speaking.

"Are you Fred the Robot?" asked the Captain.

What the Captain said is put inside speech marks.

What did you say?

Write some speech for each of these characters inside the speech marks. Remember question marks or exclamation marks go INSIDE the speech marks. *(2 marks for each correct sentence)*

"_____" asked the teacher.

"_____," called Mum.

"_____" shouted the policeman.

"_____" laughed the clown.

"_____" asked the shopkeeper.

Who said that?

It is important if we're writing a story with more than one character in it to say who is speaking. Read these lines of speech and write down who might have said them. *(1 mark for each correct answer)*

"It's time you did your homework!" called _____

"It's time for Assembly," said _____

"Hand over your money!" shouted _____

"I'll turn you into a frog!" cackled _____

"Can I help you, Sir?" asked _____

"You've got a broken arm," said _____

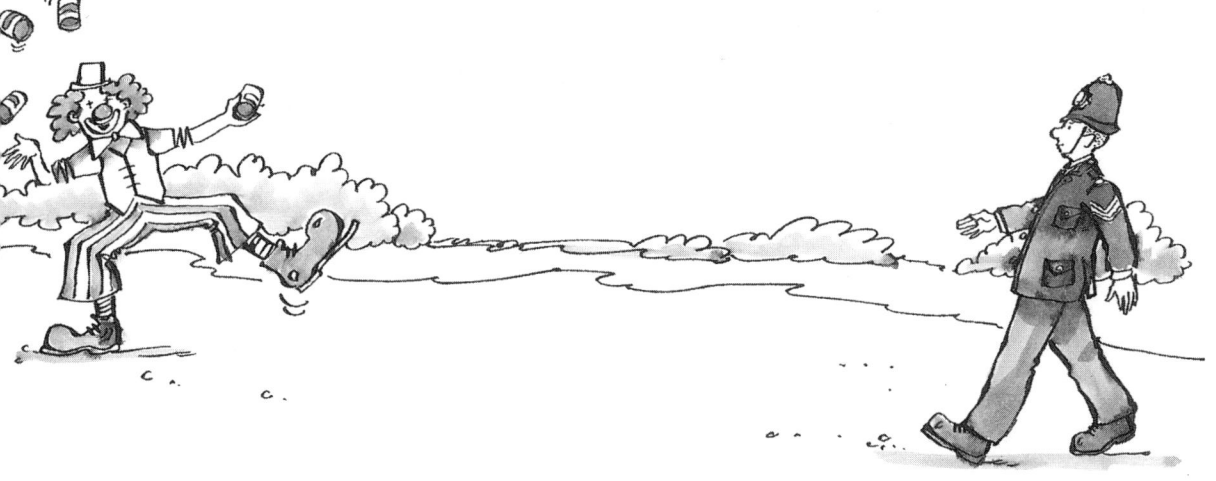

Where do they go?

The speech marks in this story are in the wrong place. Cross them out and put them in the right places. *(1 mark for each correct answer)*

Can I help you? "said the lady at the counter". Yes, "please," replied Carl. "He wanted to buy" a new bike. How much is that one? he asked. "It's £100, replied the lady." Oh dear, said "Carl", I'll have to save up my "pocket money!" Carl left the shop, but he would "get that bike, one day."

Speech bubbles

🔑 Key idea

A speech bubble is used to show who is speaking and what they have said. Speech bubbles are used in pictures, cartoons, posters and information texts. We do not use speech marks inside a speech bubble.

Perfect pets!

Write what each pet is saying in the correct speech bubble.
(5 marks for each correct answer)

"I'll fetch that stick!"   "I've laid you an egg!"   "Can I have some milk?"

Look after your pets!

Here is Jaswinder, the vet. Write in her tips for looking after your pet. There are some clues to help you in the pictures.
(15 marks)

Ways of presenting texts – BLOCK CAPITALS

Key idea

We use BLOCK CAPITALS when writing to show that something is important, scary, exciting or dangerous.
They also mark someone is shouting or giving an instruction or a warning.
STOP!   "Don't go in THERE!"

A capital idea

Write out the alphabet in BLOCK CAPITALS.
Make sure each letter is formed correctly! *(0.5 mark for each correct letter and 1 mark for the correct order)*

___ ___ ___ ___ ___ ___

___ ___ ___ ___ ___ ___

___ ___ ___ ___ ___ ___

___ ___ ___ ___ ___ ___

___ ___

The right sign

Write out these signs using BLOCK CAPITALS. Then write five more of your own. *(2 marks for each correct sign)*

Beware of the dog.   _____

_____

High Tides.   _____

_____

Open.   _____

_____

Unit 18 Commas in lists

Key idea

Commas are used to separate items in a list.

   Joe put a pencil, a rubber, a sharpener and an apple into his bag.

The last two items in a list are joined by "and" to show it is the end of this list.

Comma collections

Put the missing commas into these lists. *(1 mark for each correct comma)*

Apple orange grape and pear.
Tea coffee milk and water.
Pencil felt-tip crayon and pen.
Card envelope letter and stamp.
Plate saucer jug and cup.

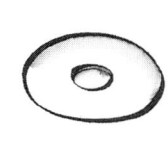

What is missing?

Write out these lists, putting in the missing commas. Remember to place an "and" between the last two items. *(1 mark for each correct comma and "and")*

Drum guitar piano recorder.
Hammer saw nail screw.
Oak ash elm willow pine.

What do you like?

Finish these lists. *(2 marks for each list)*

I like to drink _____ _____ and _____.
I don't like _____ _____ _____ _____.
I like to play _____ _____ _____ _____.
I wish I had a _____ _____ _____ _____.
I would like to go to _____ _____ _____ _____.

Unit 19 Regular past tense

🔑 Key idea

We use the past tense to say when something has already happened. Many verbs make the past tense by adding **ed**.

I wash my face – it is happening now; it is the PRESENT TENSE.

I wash**ed** my face – it happened some time ago; it is the PAST TENSE.

Back in time!

Write out these verbs turning them into the past tense by adding **ed**. *(1 mark for each correct answer)*

pull	_____	jump	_____
play	_____	push	_____
look	_____	call	_____
shout	_____	brush	_____
watch	_____	turn	_____

Drop the 'e' and add 'ed'

Make these verbs into the past tense by dropping the *e* and adding **ed**. *(0.5 mark for each correct answer)*

race	_____	skate	_____
cuddle	_____	change	_____
smile	_____	wipe	_____
wiggle	_____	hope	_____

Time for a story

Change the verbs so this story is in the past tense. *(1 mark for each correct past tense and 1 for each sentence written out correctly)*

Last Tuesday, Sophie and I play our favourite game, Tug of War. I pull very hard. I watch the rope carefully. I move my feet slowly. I call to the winner. I enjoy this game!

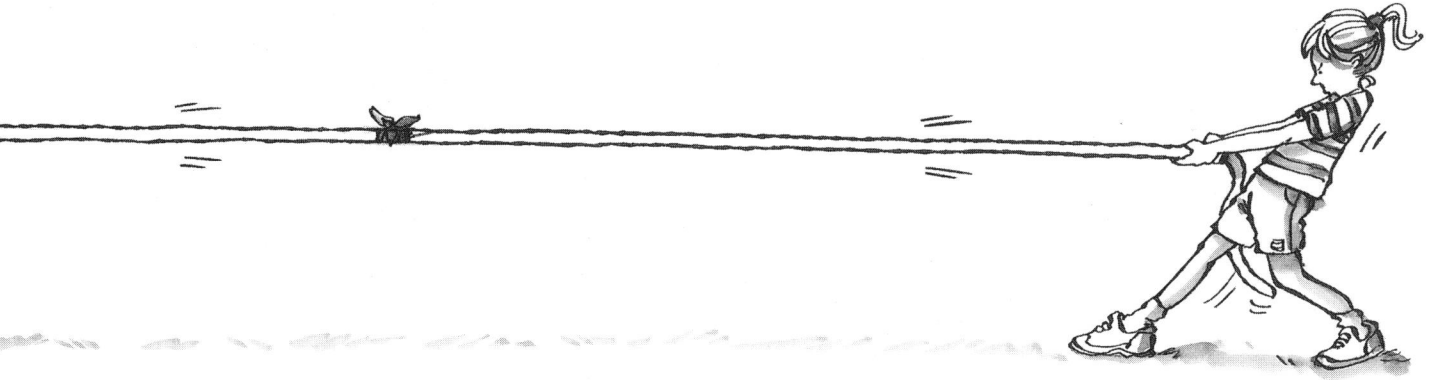

Unit 20 Tricky past tenses

🔑 Key idea

Not all verbs add **ed** to put them into the past. Verbs which do not are called **irregular** verbs.

I make a model = I made a model.

We can check by adding **ed**. If it doesn't sound right, then it must be an irregular verb.

All in the past!

Write these past tenses in the present tense. *(1 mark for each correct answer)*

For example, saw = see

went = _____
took = _____
drove = _____
came = _____
ate = _____
fought = _____
grew = _____
won = _____
slept = _____
hid = _____

Verb detective!

Underline the verbs which do not use ed to make the past tense. Check by saying each verb with ed at the end. *(0.5 mark for each correct answer)*

play	see	make	fly	wish	run	call	give	sit
drink	turn	eat	write	catch	jump	dig	tell	
paint	build	munch	ride	pick	hold	go		
chase	sing	have	shout	ring	wear			

All mixed up!

Rewrite this story, so that it uses the correct past tense.
(2 marks for each correct tense)

Yesterday Amit **go** to the seaside. He **takes** his swimming kit and he **swimmed** in the sea. He **eat** an ice cream and **writed** a postcard to his friend.

_____

_____

_____

_____

_____

_____

_____

unit 21 — Does my sentence make sense?

🔑 Key idea

Sentences must make sense and all their parts must work together.

The Princess wore his tiara = The Princess wore her tiara.

This sentence doesn't make sense as the "Princess" is wearing "his" tiara. Each part of the sentence must "agree".

We must also check that the subject and the verb "agree". The King were sad = The King was sad.

Get it right!

Choose the correct word to finish each sentence. *(1 mark for each correct answer)*

1. The King wore _____ crown. (his/her)
2. The Queen wore _____ jewels. (his/her)
3. The people _____ happy. (was/were)
4. The castle _____ very big. (is/are)
5. There _____ lots of flowers in the garden. (was/were)

Is this correct?

Underline the word that is wrong. Put the correct word in the space. *(2 marks for each correct sentence)*

1. The Prince were tired. _____
2. The boys was friends. _____
3. The King like to eat sweets. _____
4. The Queen give the Prince a pet. _____
5. It are a kitten. _____

The prince's cat

Correct the Prince's mistakes in his pet report. Check that each sentence makes sense! *(3 marks for each correct answer)*

My cat like to chase mice. It have very soft fur. There is lots of rats in the castle and my cat chases it! I think my cat are wonderful.

Unit 22: Question words

🔑 Key idea

When we write a question we often start with a question word.
A question word asks a question all by itself.
Who? Why? When? Where? What? How? These are all question words.
We always put a question mark at the end of a question.

Who or how?

Put in the correct question word to finish these questions.

(2 marks for each correct sentence)

1 _____ did you get here?
2 _____ told you that?
3 _____ old are you?
4 _____ did you do that?
5 _____ is your favourite footballer?

Interview time!

Write out a series of questions that you would like to ask a friend, your teacher or a member of your family. Use the question words given to start off each question. Make sure each one ends with a question mark. *(20 marks)*

How _____

Where _____

When _____

Who _____

What _____

32

Key Grammar is a brand new resource, specifically planned to cover all the key grammar objectives in self-contained units of work. The pupil books feature:

- clear, progressive units covering all key learning objectives
- plenty of practice and consolidation work
- opportunities to challenge and extend children's learning
- a clear mark scheme
- exercises in an appropriate context, with engaging illustrations

The workbooks provide activities for additional practice, differentiation, and homework. The important language skills coverage in Key Grammar is complemented by two associated series: Key Comprehension and Key Spelling – up-to-date and engaging resources which reinforce key teaching points and enable children to practise, consolidate and extend their learning. For further information about Key Comprehension and Key Spelling call our Customer Services Department on (+44) (0)1865 888000.

Author: Chris Wardle

Ginn
Halley Court, Jordan Hill, Oxford OX2 8EJ
a division of Harcourt Education Limited

www.myprimary.co.uk
Help and support for teachers plus the widest range of education solutions

Ginn is a registered trademark of Harcourt Education Limited

© Harcourt Education Limited 2005

This book is copyright and reproduction of the whole or part without the publishers' written permission is prohibited.

Key Grammar Workbook Starter Level
ISBN: 978 0602 20679 6
Starter Level Easy Order Pack: 978 0602 20621 5
Starter Level Workbook 6 Pack: 978 0602 20643 7

First published 2005

20 19 18 17 16
15 14

Cover illustration by Pet Gotohda
Cover design by Tom Cole
Designed by Nicki Wise, Te Marama Design
Illustrations by Andrea Pretrlik Huseinovic, Maddy McClellan, Christina Bretschneider

Printed and bound by Malaysia (CTP-VVP)

Grammar Starter Level Workbook

Contents

Unit 1	Sentence construction 1	page 2
Unit 2	Sentence construction 2	page 4
Unit 3	Sentence construction 3	page 5
Unit 4	Using full stops	page 6
Unit 5	Capital letters	page 8
Unit 6	Word order in sentences	page 10
Unit 7	Uses of capital letters	page 12
Unit 8	Linking words	page 14
Unit 9	Organisational devices	page 15
Unit 10	Question marks	page 16
Unit 12	Exclamation marks	page 18
Unit 13	Commas	page 19
Unit 14	Speech marks	page 20
Unit 15	Speech bubbles	page 22
Unit 16	Ways of presenting text	page 23
Unit 18	Commas in lists	page 24
Unit 19	Regular past tense	page 26
Unit 20	Tricky past tenses!	page 28
Unit 21	Does my sentence make sense?	page 30
Unit 22	Question words	page 32

Unit 1

Sentence construction 1

🔑 Key idea

A verb is a "doing" or a "being" word. All sentences need a verb to say what is happening.

Who's doing what?

Look at each of these pictures and write the verb which shows what the person is doing in each one. Choose the verbs from the box. *(1 mark for each correct answer)*

| singing | running | fishing | swimming | drinking |
| cooking | crying | writing | eating | kicking |

Finish the sentence

Choose a verb to complete each sentence.
(1 mark for each correct answer)

> swam   drove   ran
> danced   watched
> barked   washed
> played   drilled   changed

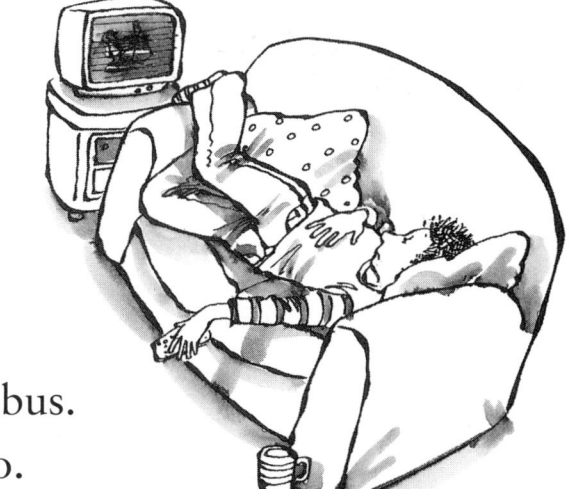

1 The lady _____ for the bus.
2 Tariq _____ at the disco.
3 Tariq _____ T.V. after school.
4 The dog _____ at the old man.
5 Tariq _____ his hands.
6 The magician _____ a bird into a rabbit!
7 The dentist _____ Tariq's tooth.
8 Tariq and Adam _____ football in the park.
9 Adam _____ in the pool.
10 Tariq's dad _____ to school in his new car.

Spot the verb!

Some of these sentences have a verb missing! Try to spot them, putting a tick or a cross after each sentence. Tick if the verb is there or put a cross if the verb is missing. *(1 mark for each correct answer)*

1 Tariq shut the door.
2 Mary the car.
3 Amy the park.
4 I saw a bird.
5 The boy seven.
6 Jill watched the film.
7 Tariq cut the string.
8 He the new cards.
9 The cup is red.
10 Tariq read two books.

Unit 2 Sentence construction 2

🔑 Key idea

A sentence is a group of words which carries a meaning.
Sentences must make sense.

    Amy walked to school.

This sentence tells us how Amy got to school. It makes sense and is a complete idea.

Correct it!

These sentences have got mixed up. Underline the wrong word and write the correct one at the end of the sentence. *(3 marks for each correct answer)*

1 The cat was barking. _____   4 The dog drank the milk. _____
2 The bear was very tiny. _____ 5 A rabbit lives in a swamp. _____
3 An ant is big and furry. _____ 6 A crocodile lives in a hutch. _____

Get it right!

These sentences do not make sense. Change the word in bold so that the sentence makes sense. *(2 marks for each correct answer)*

1 Amy **are** a very nice girl. _____
2 Tariq **have** a cat. _____
3 The dogs **has** long tails. _____
4 Dad **like** ice cream. _____
5 The **shoe** were too tight. _____
6 I think Adam **are** a very kind boy. _____

Unit 3 Sentence construction 3

Key idea

Sentences have a subject and an object.
Sentences must be clear and make sense.
The subject tells us 'who' or 'what' the sentence is about. The subject goes with the verb. The object of a sentence is the person or thing the subject is doing something to.

Who's doing what?

The subject of these sentences is missing.
Write in the subject for each one. Use the words in the box to help you. *(3 marks for each correct answer)*

1 The _____ sat in his kennel.
2 The _____ played with her kittens.
3 The _____ read a story in Assembly.
4 The _____ ate a carrot.
5 A _____ flew onto the tree.

> dog teacher
> rabbit
> cat bird

Finish the sentence

The object in each of these sentences is missing. Write in the object for each one. Use the words in the box to help you.

(3 marks for each correct answer)

1 The boy batted the _____.
2 The postman dropped a _____.
3 The dog found a long, white _____.
4 The cow chewed the _____.
5 The bird sat on the _____.

> letter bone
> ball grass
> branch

Using full stops

 **Key idea** •

A full stop marks the end of a sentence. It shows the reader where one idea ends.

Amy wanted a new book. She went to the shops to buy one. Two full stops are used, as there are two ideas, each in their own sentence.

Spot the stop! •

Look at these sentences. The full stop is in the wrong place. Cross it out and put it in the right place. *(1 mark for each correct answer)*

1 Adam. went to the shops
2 Amy saw. her sister
3 The man walked. into town
4 Tariq played with his friend. Sam
5 The lady had two. bags of shopping
6 Adam helped in the. garden
7 The. cow was in the field.
8 Amy flew her. kite on Saturday
9 John saw the. fireworks
10 The lady sang a beautiful. song

Find the sentence

Some words have been added to the ends of these sentences. Put in the full stop to show where the sentence should end and cross out the extra words! *(1 mark for each correct answer)*

For example: John was happy. ~~doors shops~~

1 Tariq enjoyed his party waits says
2 Amy watched the film snow open
3 The doctor went to see Adam shake David Hamid
4 The shops were very busy time cooking frosty
5 John went fishing with his dad baby shoes Tuesday
6 Amy saw a magic show ties paper poster
7 The King spoke to the crowd strange book cows
8 Yesterday Tariq built a model glass coats
9 The owl hooted in the night cards
10 It was a very hot day windows newspaper

Correct the story

There are ten missing full stops in this short story. Put in the full stops so that the story makes sense. *(1 mark for each correct answer)*

Amy was reading in her bedroom Her mum came in and asked her if she wanted to go to the fair Amy was so excited Later that afternoon Amy and her mum set off When they got there Amy saw the dodgems Amy wanted to have a go Her mum agreed and she had two rides Then Amy saw the ghost train Amy was a bit scared but she had a ride It was lots of fun

Unit 5 Capital letters

Key idea

Capital letters are used to show the start of a sentence and to identify proper nouns, such as names of people.

Everyone saw the clowns and Freddy was the biggest clown of all. **Everyone** starts with a capital letter as it begins the sentence. **Freddy** begins with a capital letter as it is a name.

Send in the clowns!

Write out the names of the clowns. Each name should start with a capital letter. *(1 mark for each correct answer)*

| coco | daisy | billy | sidney | freddy |
| joey | archie | peggy | winston | smartie |

_____   _____

_____   _____

_____   _____

_____   _____

_____   _____

A capital idea!

Write out each sentence remembering to start with a capital letter.

(1 mark for each correct answer)

1. the tent was very big. _____
2. joey had orange hair. _____
3. the tickets cost £3.50. _____
4. a lady was selling ice creams. _____
5. the clowns made us laugh. _____
6. i laughed at the clowns. _____
7. freddy fell off his chair! _____
8. mum got me a clown badge. _____
9. it was an exciting show. _____
10. i would like to see it again. _____

What happened next?

Write out five sentences about some funny things the clowns might have done. Remember to start each one with a capital letter. Use these words to help you: clown, mess, threw, pies, water, car, squirted and crash. *(2 marks for each correct sentence)*

_____
_____
_____
_____
_____

Unit 6: Word order in sentences

Key idea

Each sentence has a subject and an object. Words in a sentence must be in the correct order to make sense.

An alien flew down to Earth.

This sentence makes sense. The words are in the correct order. The sentence tells us something. It conveys an idea.

Alien message

Translate this alien message by putting the words into the correct order in each sentence. *(2 marks for each correct sentence)*

Venus from we send greetings. Peace we come in. friends your are we. Chocolate like we. Large is our very spaceship.

_____

_____

_____

Alien objects

Complete this message from the aliens by putting in an object for each sentence. *(1 mark for each correct answer)*

We have read all your _____

We have tasted your _____

Our spaceship landed on the _____

We write with long _____

We would like to eat some _____

Our planet crashed into _____

We have looked at your _____

Our computer has tested your _____

We are excited by your _____

Our troops have been into the _____

Write to the aliens!

Make up your own message for the aliens. You will need to write out five short sentences, changing the word order so that it does not make sense to humans. Make sure you include all the words you will need in each sentence. Make sure each sentence has a subject. *(2 marks for each correct sentence)*

For example:

Where have you come from? = Come from have where you?

_____

_____

_____

_____

unit 7 Capital letters

Key idea

Capital letters are used to show the start of a sentence, and to identify proper nouns – names of people, places, titles and times.

Capitalise!

Write these words below, so that each one starts with a capital letter. *(1 mark for each correct answer)*

may _____   rome _____

i _____   fred _____

paul _____   tuesday _____

february _____   sally _____

sunday _____   august _____

Choose a word!

Write eight words that need to start with a capital letter. You might choose the names of people, places, days or months of the year. *(1 mark for each correct answer)*

_____   _____

_____   _____

_____   _____

_____   _____

Now write the name of your favourite book or story. *(2 marks)*

_____

Which is right?

Adam has got mixed up and written every word below with a capital letter! Copy it out correctly, keeping only the correct capitals. *(0.5 mark for each correction)*

On Sunday I Saw My Friend Sam. He Has A Dog Called Scruffy. We Took Scruffy To The Park On Sunshine Street. It Was Lots Of Fun! We Will Go Again Next Sunday.

_____

_____

_____

_____

Unit 8 Linking words

🔑 Key idea

We can join short sentences together to make longer, more interesting sentences. We use link words like AND, SO or BUT.

The lion was hungry. The lion ate some meat.
= The lion was hungry so he ate some meat.

We do not need the second "The lion" as we know he is the subject of the sentence.

Zoo report

Amy wrote a report of her trip to the zoo. Join these pairs of sentences together using "and". *(3 marks for each correct sentence)*

1 I put on my coat. I went to the zoo. _____
2 I carried my camera. I took photos. _____
3 I saw the zebras. I saw the chimps. _____
4 I fed the rabbits. I fed the ducks. _____
5 The chimps were noisy. They were funny. _____

All mixed up!

Choose from "and", "so", "because" or "but" to join these sentences. *(3 marks for each correct sentence)*

1 I am going home. It is too late to go to the zoo. _____
2 You are helping me. She is not. _____
3 I love the chimps. They are funny animals. _____
4 I ate an ice cream. I ate a hot dog. _____
5 I wanted to buy a T-shirt. I didn't have enough money. _____

Unit 9 Organisational devices

Key idea

We use short sentences, letters, numbers or bullet points and pictures to set out instructions.

Set it out!

Write out these instructions so that they are easy to follow.
(15 marks)

Giving your puppy a bath. First, fill the bath half way with warm water. Put your puppy in the bath and wash it with soap and water. Rinse the puppy carefully. Lift your puppy out of the bath. Dry your puppy with a towel and brush its coat.

_____   _____

_____   _____

_____   _____

Make a snowman

These instructions are mixed up. Read them carefully and put a letter from "a" to "f" next to each one to order them. *(15 marks)*

a.   Firstly, roll a large ball of snow.
___ Finally, put a hat on his head and a scarf around his neck.
___ Roll a smaller ball and put it on top for a head.
___ Push in two sticks for arms and put gloves on for hands.
___ Add two stones and a carrot to the smaller ball for a face.

Unit 10 Question marks

Key idea

A question mark is used to show a question.

It comes at the end of the question.

You do not need a full stop after a question mark.

   What is your name?

   How old are you?

These are both questions, as they need an answer.

Here we go!

Add question marks to the end of these five questions.
Make sure you form the question mark carefully. *(1 mark for each correct answer)*

1   Is it a long trip
2   Are you going by plane
3   Do you have two bags
4   Will the plane land in Glasgow
5   Is this a jumbo jet

Find that question!

Look through one of your reading books and write down five questions that you find in the story. Remember to begin each with a capital letter and put a question mark at the end.
(10 marks)

_____

_____

_____

_____

_____

Interview a pilot!

Here are five answers a pilot gave, but what were the questions? Look at the answers and write the question you think he was asked. *(3 marks for each correct question)*

_____

I have been a pilot for 4 years.

_____

My favourite airport is in Paris.

_____

Yes, I do like my uniform.

_____

I wanted to be a pilot when I was young.

_____

I was born in Manchester.

Unit 12: Exclamation marks

Key idea

We use exclamation marks to show that something scary, exciting or surprising has happened. They are also used to show that someone in a story is shouting or something is loud.

Read the signs!

These signs have their exclamation marks missing. Copy them carefully and add the exclamation marks. *(2 marks for each one)*

DANGER

Falling Rocks

Do not swim here

Private

Do not enter

The spooky castle

There are ten exclamation marks missing from this short story. Read it carefully and put them in. *(1 mark for each correct answer)*

Aneena went into the old, spooky castle. CRASH. The old clock fell off the wall all by itself. Aneena thought it must be a ghost. THUD. The door slammed shut by itself. BOOM. WHOOSH. A cannon on the roof went off. Aneena was very scared, so she pulled the door but it was stuck.

Finish the story!

Write out the end of Aneena's story. *(10 marks)*

Commas

Key idea

Commas are used to add extra information or to create a pause. They break up longer sentences into smaller parts.

Quickly, Davina locked the door!

Exciting sentences!

Complete these sentences in an exciting way, by finishing each sentence after the comma. *(3 marks for each correct sentence)*

Suddenly, _____

Just at that moment, _____

All at once, _____

The door slowly opened, _____

Although it was dark, _____

Finally, _____

Commas in pairs!

Place the commas where you think extra information has been added to each sentence. *(2 marks for each correct sentence)*

The clock which was very old did not work.

Davina who was wearing a red dress hid behind the red curtains.

The rain which had been pouring all day finally stopped.

Davina in her loudest voice shouted from behind the curtains!

Everyone including Davina's mum was very surprised!

Everyone including Davina had to walk home through the rain.

Unit 14 Speech marks

Key idea

We use speech marks to show when someone is speaking.

"Are you Fred the Robot?" asked the Captain.

What the Captain said is put inside speech marks.

What did you say?

Write some speech for each of these characters inside the speech marks. Remember question marks or exclamation marks go INSIDE the speech marks. *(2 marks for each correct sentence)*

"_____" asked the teacher.

"_____," called Mum.

"_____" shouted the policeman.

"_____" laughed the clown.

"_____" asked the shopkeeper.

Who said that?

It is important if we're writing a story with more than one character in it to say who is speaking. Read these lines of speech and write down who might have said them. *(1 mark for each correct answer)*

"It's time you did your homework!" called _____

"It's time for Assembly," said _____

"Hand over your money!" shouted _____

"I'll turn you into a frog!" cackled _____

"Can I help you, Sir?" asked _____

"You've got a broken arm," said _____

Where do they go?

The speech marks in this story are in the wrong place. Cross them out and put them in the right places. *(1 mark for each correct answer)*

Can I help you? "said the lady at the counter". Yes, "please," replied Carl. "He wanted to buy" a new bike. How much is that one? he asked. "It's £100, replied the lady." Oh dear, said "Carl", I'll have to save up my "pocket money!" Carl left the shop, but he would "get that bike, one day."

Speech bubbles

🔑 Key idea

A speech bubble is used to show who is speaking and what they have said. Speech bubbles are used in pictures, cartoons, posters and information texts. We do not use speech marks inside a speech bubble.

Perfect pets!

Write what each pet is saying in the correct speech bubble.
(5 marks for each correct answer)

"I'll fetch that stick!"   "I've laid you an egg!"   "Can I have some milk?"

Look after your pets!

Here is Jaswinder, the vet. Write in her tips for looking after your pet. There are some clues to help you in the pictures.
(15 marks)

Unit 16: Ways of presenting texts – BLOCK CAPITALS

Key idea

We use BLOCK CAPITALS when writing to show that something is important, scary, exciting or dangerous.
They also mark someone is shouting or giving an instruction or a warning.

STOP!   "Don't go in THERE!"

A capital idea

Write out the alphabet in BLOCK CAPITALS.
Make sure each letter is formed correctly! *(0.5 mark for each correct letter and 1 mark for the correct order)*

____ ____ ____ ____ ____ ____ ____

____ ____ ____ ____ ____ ____ ____

____ ____ ____ ____ ____ ____ ____

____ ____ ____ ____ ____ ____ ____

____

The right sign

Write out these signs using BLOCK CAPITALS. Then write five more of your own. *(2 marks for each correct sign)*

Beware of the dog.   _____

_____

High Tides.   _____

_____

Open.   _____

_____

# Unit 18 Commas in lists

Key idea

Commas are used to separate items in a list.

Joe put a pencil, a rubber, a sharpener and an apple into his bag. The last two items in a list are joined by "and" to show it is the end of this list.

Comma collections

Put the missing commas into these lists. *(1 mark for each correct comma)*

Apple orange grape and pear.
Tea coffee milk and water.
Pencil felt-tip crayon and pen.
Card envelope letter and stamp.
Plate saucer jug and cup.

 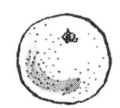

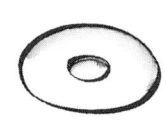

What is missing?

Write out these lists, putting in the missing commas. Remember to place an "and" between the last two items. *(1 mark for each correct comma and "and")*

Drum guitar piano recorder.
Hammer saw nail screw.
Oak ash elm willow pine.

What do you like?

Finish these lists. *(2 marks for each list)*

I like to drink _____ _____ and _____.
I don't like _____ _____ ___ _____.
I like to play _____ _____ ___ _____.
I wish I had a _____ _____ ___ _____.
I would like to go to _____ _____ ___ _____.

unit 19 Regular past tense

🔑 Key idea

We use the past tense to say when something has already happened. Many verbs make the past tense by adding **ed**.

I wash my face – it is happening now; it is the PRESENT TENSE.

I wash**ed** my face – it happened some time ago; it is the PAST TENSE.

Back in time!

Write out these verbs turning them into the past tense by adding **ed**. *(1 mark for each correct answer)*

pull	_____	jump	_____
play	_____	push	_____
look	_____	call	_____
shout	_____	brush	_____
watch	_____	turn	_____

Drop the 'e' and add 'ed'

Make these verbs into the past tense by dropping the e and adding **ed**. *(0.5 mark for each correct answer)*

race	_____	skate	_____
cuddle	_____	change	_____
smile	_____	wipe	_____
wiggle	_____	hope	_____

Time for a story

Change the verbs so this story is in the past tense. *(1 mark for each correct past tense and 1 for each sentence written out correctly)*

Last Tuesday, Sophie and I play our favourite game, Tug of War. I pull very hard. I watch the rope carefully. I move my feet slowly. I call to the winner. I enjoy this game!

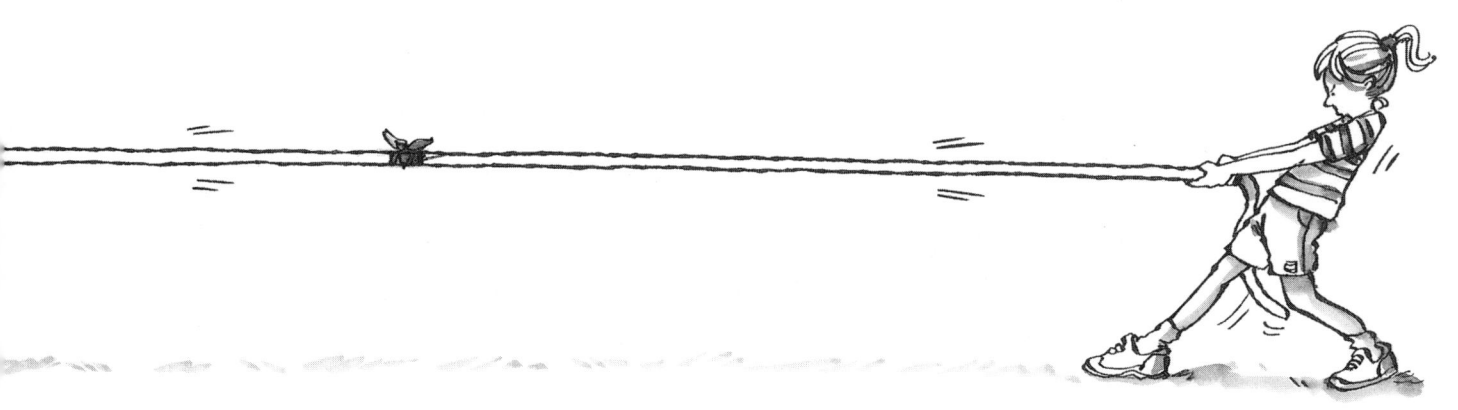

unit 20 Tricky past tenses

Key idea

Not all verbs add **ed** to put them into the past. Verbs which do not are called **irregular** verbs.

I make a model = I made a model.

We can check by adding **ed**. If it doesn't sound right, then it must be an irregular verb.

All in the past!

Write these past tenses in the present tense. *(1 mark for each correct answer)*

For example, saw = see

went = _____
took = _____
drove = _____
came = _____
ate = _____
fought = _____
grew = _____
won = _____
slept = _____
hid = _____

28

Verb detective!

Underline the verbs which do not use ed to make the past tense. Check by saying each verb with ed at the end. *(0.5 mark for each correct answer)*

> play   see   make   fly   wish   run   call   give   sit
> drink   turn   eat   write   catch   jump   dig   tell
> paint   build   munch   ride   pick   hold   go
> chase   sing   have   shout   ring   wear

All mixed up!

Rewrite this story, so that it uses the correct past tense.
(2 marks for each correct tense)

Yesterday Amit **go** to the seaside. He **takes** his swimming kit and he **swimmed** in the sea. He **eat** an ice cream and **writed** a postcard to his friend.

Unit 21 Does my sentence make sense?

🔑 Key idea

Sentences must make sense and all their parts must work together.

The Princess wore his tiara = The Princess wore her tiara.

This sentence doesn't make sense as the "Princess" is wearing "his" tiara. Each part of the sentence must "agree".

We must also check that the subject and the verb "agree". The King were sad = The King was sad.

Get it right!

Choose the correct word to finish each sentence. *(1 mark for each correct answer)*

1 The King wore _____ crown. (his/her)
2 The Queen wore _____ jewels. (his/her)
3 The people _____ happy. (was/were)
4 The castle _____ very big. (is/are)
5 There _____ lots of flowers in the garden. (was/were)

Is this correct?

Underline the word that is wrong. Put the correct word in the space. *(2 marks for each correct sentence)*

1 The Prince were tired. _____
2 The boys was friends. _____
3 The King like to eat sweets. _____
4 The Queen give the Prince a pet. _____
5 It are a kitten. _____

The prince's cat

Correct the Prince's mistakes in his pet report. Check that each sentence makes sense! *(3 marks for each correct answer)*

My cat like to chase mice. It have very soft fur. There is lots of rats in the castle and my cat chases it! I think my cat are wonderful.

 # unit 22 Question words

🗝 Key idea

When we write a question we often start with a question word. A question word asks a question all by itself.
Who? Why? When? Where? What? How? These are all question words.
We always put a question mark at the end of a question.

Who or how?

Put in the correct question word to finish these questions.

(2 marks for each correct sentence)

1 _____ did you get here?
2 _____ told you that?
3 _____ old are you?
4 _____ did you do that?
5 _____ is your favourite footballer?

Interview time!

Write out a series of questions that you would like to ask a friend, your teacher or a member of your family. Use the question words given to start off each question. Make sure each one ends with a question mark. *(20 marks)*

How _____
Where _____
When _____
Who _____
What _____

Key Grammar is a brand new resource, specifically planned to cover all the key grammar objectives in self-contained units of work. The pupil books feature:

- clear, progressive units covering all key learning objectives
- plenty of practice and consolidation work
- opportunities to challenge and extend children's learning
- a clear mark scheme
- exercises in an appropriate context, with engaging illustrations

The workbooks provide activities for additional practice, differentiation, and homework. The important language skills coverage in **Key Grammar** is complemented by two associated series: **Key Comprehension** and **Key Spelling** – up-to-date and engaging resources which reinforce key teaching points and enable children to practise, consolidate and extend their learning. For further information about **Key Comprehension** and **Key Spelling** call our Customer Services Department on **(+44) (0)1865 888000**.

ISBN 978-0-602206-79-6

Key Grammar is a brand new resource, specifically planned to cover all the key grammar objectives in self-contained units of work. The pupil books feature:

- clear, progressive units covering all key learning objectives
- plenty of practice and consolidation work
- opportunities to challenge and extend children's learning
- a clear mark scheme
- exercises in an appropriate context, with engaging illustrations

The workbooks provide activities for additional practice, differentiation, and homework. The important language skills coverage in **Key Grammar** is complemented by two associated series: **Key Comprehension** and **Key Spelling** – up-to-date and engaging resources which reinforce key teaching points and enable children to practise, consolidate and extend their learning. For further information about **Key Comprehension** and **Key Spelling** call our Customer Services Department on **(+44) (0)1865 888000**.

ISBN 978-0-602206-79-6

# Unit 22

Question words

Key idea

When we write a question we often start with a question word.
A question word asks a question all by itself.
Who? Why? When? Where? What? How? These are all question words.
We always put a question mark at the end of a question.

Who or how?

Put in the correct question word to finish these questions.
(2 marks for each correct sentence)

1 _____ did you get here?
2 _____ told you that?
3 _____ old are you?
4 _____ did you do that?
5 _____ is your favourite footballer?

Interview time!

Write out a series of questions that you would like to ask a friend, your teacher or a member of your family. Use the question words given to start off each question. Make sure each one ends with a question mark. *(20 marks)*

How _____
Where _____
When _____
Who _____
What _____

The prince's cat

Correct the Prince's mistakes in his pet report. Check that each sentence makes sense! *(3 marks for each correct answer)*

My cat like to chase mice. It have very soft fur. There is lots of rats in the castle and my cat chases it! I think my cat are wonderful.

_____

_____

_____

_____

_____

_____

_____

Unit 21

Does my sentence make sense?

Key idea

Sentences must make sense and all their parts must work together.

The Princess wore his tiara = The Princess wore her tiara.

This sentence doesn't make sense as the "Princess" is wearing "his" tiara. Each part of the sentence must "agree".

We must also check that the subject and the verb "agree". The King were sad = The King was sad.

Get it right!

Choose the correct word to finish each sentence. *(1 mark for each correct answer)*

1 The King wore _____ crown. (his/her)
2 The Queen wore _____ jewels. (his/her)
3 The people _____ happy. (was/were)
4 The castle _____ very big. (is/are)
5 There _____ lots of flowers in the garden. (was/were)

Is this correct?

Underline the word that is wrong. Put the correct word in the space. *(2 marks for each correct sentence)*

1 The Prince were tired. _____
2 The boys was friends. _____
3 The King like to eat sweets. _____
4 The Queen give the Prince a pet. _____
5 It are a kitten. _____

Verb detective!

Underline the verbs which do not use ed to make the past tense. Check by saying each verb with ed at the end. *(0.5 mark for each correct answer)*

play	see	make	fly	wish	run	call	give	sit
drink	turn	eat	write	catch	jump	dig	tell	
paint	build	munch	ride	pick	hold	go		
chase	sing	have	shout	ring	wear			

All mixed up!

Rewrite this story, so that it uses the correct past tense.
(2 marks for each correct tense)

Yesterday Amit **go** to the seaside. He **takes** his swimming kit and he **swimmed** in the sea. He **eat** an ice cream and **writed** a postcard to his friend.

_____

_____

_____

_____

_____

_____

_____

unit 20 Tricky past tenses

🔑 Key idea

Not all verbs add **ed** to put them into the past. Verbs which do not are called **irregular** verbs.

I make a model = I made a model.

We can check by adding **ed**. If it doesn't sound right, then it must be an irregular verb.

All in the past!

Write these past tenses in the present tense. *(1 mark for each correct answer)*

For example, saw = see

went = _____
took = _____
drove = _____
came = _____
ate = _____
fought = _____
grew = _____
won = _____
slept = _____
hid = _____

28

Time for a story

Change the verbs so this story is in the past tense. *(1 mark for each correct past tense and 1 for each sentence written out correctly)*

Last Tuesday, Sophie and I play our favourite game, Tug of War. I pull very hard. I watch the rope carefully. I move my feet slowly. I call to the winner. I enjoy this game!

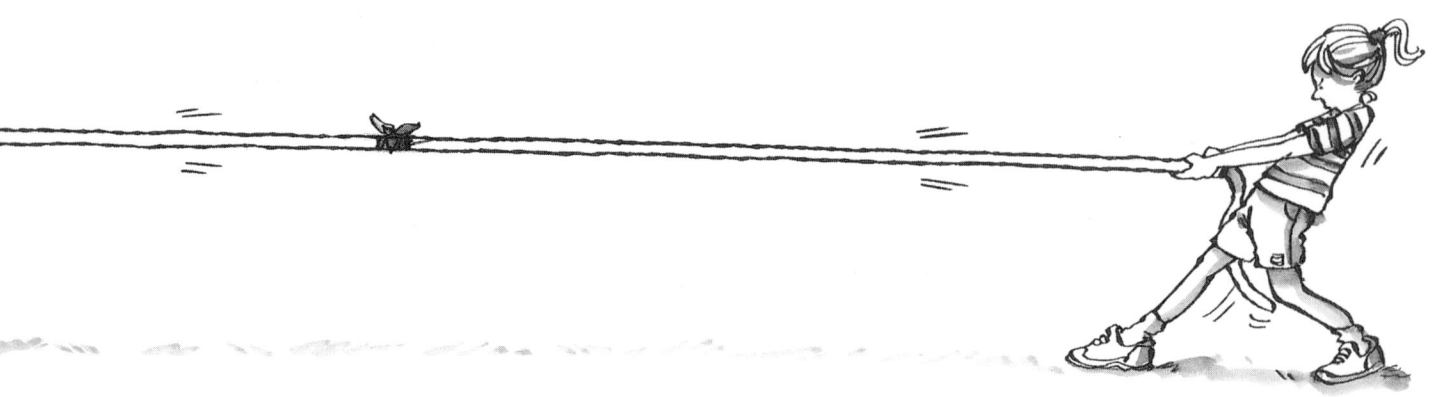

Regular past tense

Key idea

We use the past tense to say when something has already happened. Many verbs make the past tense by adding **ed**.

I wash my face – it is happening now; it is the PRESENT TENSE.

I wash**ed** my face – it happened some time ago; it is the PAST TENSE.

Back in time!

Write out these verbs turning them into the past tense by adding **ed**. *(1 mark for each correct answer)*

pull _____   jump _____
play _____   push _____
look _____   call _____
shout _____ brush _____
watch _____ turn _____

Drop the 'e' and add 'ed'

Make these verbs into the past tense by dropping the e and adding **ed**. *(0.5 mark for each correct answer)*

race _____   skate _____
cuddle _____ change _____
smile _____ wipe _____
wiggle _____ hope _____

What is missing?

Write out these lists, putting in the missing commas. Remember to place an "and" between the last two items. *(1 mark for each correct comma and "and")*

Drum guitar piano recorder.
Hammer saw nail screw.
Oak ash elm willow pine.

What do you like?

Finish these lists. *(2 marks for each list)*

I like to drink _____ _____ and _____.
I don't like _____ _____ ___ _____.
I like to play _____ _____ ___ _____.
I wish I had a _____ _____ ___ _____.
I would like to go to _____ _____ ___ _____.

Unit 18 Commas in lists

🔑 Key idea

Commas are used to separate items in a list.

    Joe put a pencil, a rubber, a sharpener and an apple into his bag.

The last two items in a list are joined by "and" to show it is the end of this list.

Comma collections

Put the missing commas into these lists. *(1 mark for each correct comma)*

Apple orange grape and pear.
Tea coffee milk and water.
Pencil felt-tip crayon and pen.
Card envelope letter and stamp.
Plate saucer jug and cup.

Ways of presenting texts – BLOCK CAPITALS

Key idea

We use BLOCK CAPITALS when writing to show that something is important, scary, exciting or dangerous.
They also mark someone is shouting or giving an instruction or a warning.
STOP!   "Don't go in THERE!"

A capital idea

Write out the alphabet in BLOCK CAPITALS.
Make sure each letter is formed correctly! *(0.5 mark for each correct letter and 1 mark for the correct order)*

___ ___ ___ ___ ___

___ ___ ___ ___ ___

___ ___ ___ ___ ___

___ ___ ___ ___ ___

___ ___

The right sign

Write out these signs using BLOCK CAPITALS. Then write five more of your own. *(2 marks for each correct sign)*

Beware of the dog.   _____

_____

High Tides.

_____

_____

Open.

_____

_____

Speech bubbles

 **Key idea**

A speech bubble is used to show who is speaking and what they have said. Speech bubbles are used in pictures, cartoons, posters and information texts. We do not use speech marks inside a speech bubble.

Perfect pets!

Write what each pet is saying in the correct speech bubble.

(5 marks for each correct answer)

"I'll fetch that stick!"   "I've laid you an egg!"   "Can I have some milk?"

Look after your pets!

Here is Jaswinder, the vet. Write in her tips for looking after your pet. There are some clues to help you in the pictures.

(15 marks)

Who said that?

It is important if we're writing a story with more than one character in it to say who is speaking. Read these lines of speech and write down who might have said them. *(1 mark for each correct answer)*

"It's time you did your homework!" called _____

"It's time for Assembly," said _____

"Hand over your money!" shouted _____

"I'll turn you into a frog!" cackled _____

"Can I help you, Sir?" asked _____

"You've got a broken arm," said _____

Where do they go?

The speech marks in this story are in the wrong place. Cross them out and put them in the right places. *(1 mark for each correct answer)*

Can I help you? "said the lady at the counter". Yes, "please," replied Carl. "He wanted to buy" a new bike. How much is that one? he asked. "It's £100, replied the lady." Oh dear, said "Carl", I'll have to save up my "pocket money!" Carl left the shop, but he would "get that bike, one day."

Unit 14 Speech marks

Key idea

We use speech marks to show when someone is speaking.

"Are you Fred the Robot?" asked the Captain.

What the Captain said is put inside speech marks.

What did you say?

Write some speech for each of these characters inside the speech marks. Remember question marks or exclamation marks go INSIDE the speech marks. *(2 marks for each correct sentence)*

"_____" asked the teacher.

"_____," called Mum.

"_____" shouted the policeman.

"_____" laughed the clown.

"_____" asked the shopkeeper.

Commas

Key idea

Commas are used to add extra information or to create a pause. They break up longer sentences into smaller parts.

Quickly, Davina locked the door!

Exciting sentences!

Complete these sentences in an exciting way, by finishing each sentence after the comma. *(3 marks for each correct sentence)*

Suddenly, _____

Just at that moment, _____

All at once, _____

The door slowly opened, _____

Although it was dark, _____

Finally, _____

Commas in pairs!

Place the commas where you think extra information has been added to each sentence. *(2 marks for each correct sentence)*

The clock which was very old did not work.

Davina who was wearing a red dress hid behind the red curtains.

The rain which had been pouring all day finally stopped.

Davina in her loudest voice shouted from behind the curtains!

Everyone including Davina's mum was very surprised!

Everyone including Davina had to walk home through the rain.

Exclamation marks

Key idea

We use exclamation marks to show that something scary, exciting or surprising has happened. They are also used to show that someone in a story is shouting or something is loud.

Read the signs!

These signs have their exclamation marks missing. Copy them carefully and add the exclamation marks. *(2 marks for each one)*

DANGER   _____

Falling Rocks   _____

Do not swim here _____

Private   _____

Do not enter   _____

The spooky castle

There are ten exclamation marks missing from this short story. Read it carefully and put them in. *(1 mark for each correct answer)*

Aneena went into the old, spooky castle. CRASH. The old clock fell off the wall all by itself. Aneena thought it must be a ghost. THUD. The door slammed shut by itself. BOOM. WHOOSH. A cannon on the roof went off. Aneena was very scared, so she pulled the door but it was stuck.

Finish the story!

Write out the end of Aneena's story. *(10 marks)*

Find that question!

Look through one of your reading books and write down five questions that you find in the story. Remember to begin each with a capital letter and put a question mark at the end.
(10 marks)

_____

_____

_____

_____

_____

Interview a pilot!

Here are five answers a pilot gave, but what were the questions? Look at the answers and write the question you think he was asked. *(3 marks for each correct question)*

_____

I have been a pilot for 4 years.

_____

My favourite airport is in Paris.

_____

Yes, I do like my uniform.

_____

I wanted to be a pilot when I was young.

_____

I was born in Manchester.

unit 10 Question marks

 **Key idea**

A question mark is used to show a question.
It comes at the end of the question.
You do not need a full stop after a question mark.

> What is your name?
>
> How old are you?

These are both questions, as they need an answer.

Here we go!

Add question marks to the end of these five questions.
Make sure you form the question mark carefully. *(1 mark for each correct answer)*

1. Is it a long trip
2. Are you going by plane
3. Do you have two bags
4. Will the plane land in Glasgow
5. Is this a jumbo jet

Unit 9 Organisational devices

🔑 Key idea

We use short sentences, letters, numbers or bullet points and pictures to set out instructions.

Set it out!

Write out these instructions so that they are easy to follow.
(15 marks)

Giving your puppy a bath. First, fill the bath half way with warm water. Put your puppy in the bath and wash it with soap and water. Rinse the puppy carefully. Lift your puppy out of the bath. Dry your puppy with a towel and brush its coat.

_____   _____

_____   _____

_____   _____

Make a snowman

These instructions are mixed up. Read them carefully and put a letter from "a" to "f" next to each one to order them. *(15 marks)*

- a.   Firstly, roll a large ball of snow.
- ___ Finally, put a hat on his head and a scarf around his neck.
- ___ Roll a smaller ball and put it on top for a head.
- ___ Push in two sticks for arms and put gloves on for hands.
- ___ Add two stones and a carrot to the smaller ball for a face.

Unit 8 Linking words

🔑 Key idea

We can join short sentences together to make longer, more interesting sentences. We use link words like AND, SO or BUT.

The lion was hungry. The lion ate some meat.
= The lion was hungry so he ate some meat.

We do not need the second "The lion" as we know he is the subject of the sentence.

Zoo report

Amy wrote a report of her trip to the zoo. Join these pairs of sentences together using "and". *(3 marks for each correct sentence)*

1. I put on my coat. I went to the zoo. _____
2. I carried my camera. I took photos. _____
3. I saw the zebras. I saw the chimps. _____
4. I fed the rabbits. I fed the ducks. _____
5. The chimps were noisy. They were funny. _____

All mixed up!

Choose from "and", "so", "because" or "but" to join these sentences. *(3 marks for each correct sentence)*

1. I am going home. It is too late to go to the zoo. _____
2. You are helping me. She is not. _____
3. I love the chimps. They are funny animals. _____
4. I ate an ice cream. I ate a hot dog. _____
5. I wanted to buy a T-shirt. I didn't have enough money. _____

Choose a word!

Write eight words that need to start with a capital letter. You might choose the names of people, places, days or months of the year. *(1 mark for each correct answer)*

_____   _____

_____   _____

_____   _____

_____   _____

Now write the name of your favourite book or story. *(2 marks)*

_____

Which is right?

Adam has got mixed up and written every word below with a capital letter! Copy it out correctly, keeping only the correct capitals. *(0.5 mark for each correction)*

On Sunday I Saw My Friend Sam. He Has A Dog Called Scruffy. We Took Scruffy To The Park On Sunshine Street. It Was Lots Of Fun! We Will Go Again Next Sunday.

_____

_____

_____

_____

unit 7 Capital letters

Key idea

Capital letters are used to show the start of a sentence, and to identify proper nouns – names of people, places, titles and times.

Capitalise!

Write these words below, so that each one starts with a capital letter. *(1 mark for each correct answer)*

may _____   rome _____

i _____   fred _____

paul _____   tuesday _____

february _____   sally _____

sunday _____   august _____

Alien objects

Complete this message from the aliens by putting in an object for each sentence. *(1 mark for each correct answer)*

We have read all your _____

We have tasted your _____

Our spaceship landed on the _____

We write with long _____

We would like to eat some _____

Our planet crashed into _____

We have looked at your _____

Our computer has tested your _____

We are excited by your _____

Our troops have been into the _____

Write to the aliens!

Make up your own message for the aliens. You will need to write out five short sentences, changing the word order so that it does not make sense to humans. Make sure you include all the words you will need in each sentence. Make sure each sentence has a subject. *(2 marks for each correct sentence)*

For example:

Where have you come from? = Come from have where you?

_____

_____

_____

_____

Unit 6 — Word order in sentences

Key idea

Each sentence has a subject and an object. Words in a sentence must be in the correct order to make sense.

   An alien flew down to Earth.

This sentence makes sense. The words are in the correct order. The sentence tells us something. It conveys an idea.

Alien message

Translate this alien message by putting the words into the correct order in each sentence. *(2 marks for each correct sentence)*

Venus from we send greetings. Peace we come in. friends your are we. Chocolate like we. Large is our very spaceship.

_____

_____

_____

A capital idea!

Write out each sentence remembering to start with a capital letter.

(1 mark for each correct answer)

1   the tent was very big. _____
2   joey had orange hair. _____
3   the tickets cost £3.50. _____
4   a lady was selling ice creams. _____
5   the clowns made us laugh. _____
6   i laughed at the clowns. _____
7   freddy fell off his chair! _____
8   mum got me a clown badge. _____
9   it was an exciting show. _____
10 i would like to see it again. _____

What happened next?

Write out five sentences about some funny things the clowns might have done. Remember to start each one with a capital letter. Use these words to help you: clown, mess, threw, pies, water, car, squirted and crash. *(2 marks for each correct sentence)*

_____

_____

_____

_____

_____

Unit 5 Capital letters

Key idea

Capital letters are used to show the start of a sentence and to identify proper nouns, such as names of people.

Everyone saw the clowns and Freddy was the biggest clown of all. **Everyone** starts with a capital letter as it begins the sentence. **Freddy** begins with a capital letter as it is a name.

Send in the clowns!

Write out the names of the clowns. Each name should start with a capital letter. *(1 mark for each correct answer)*

| coco | daisy | billy | sidney | freddy |
| joey | archie | peggy | winston | smartie |

_____   _____

_____   _____

_____   _____

_____   _____

_____   _____

Find the sentence

Some words have been added to the ends of these sentences. Put in the full stop to show where the sentence should end and cross out the extra words! *(1 mark for each correct answer)*

For example: John was happy. ~~doors shops~~

1 Tariq enjoyed his party waits says
2 Amy watched the film snow open
3 The doctor went to see Adam shake David Hamid
4 The shops were very busy time cooking frosty
5 John went fishing with his dad baby shoes Tuesday
6 Amy saw a magic show ties paper poster
7 The King spoke to the crowd strange book cows
8 Yesterday Tariq built a model glass coats
9 The owl hooted in the night cards
10 It was a very hot day windows newspaper

Correct the story

There are ten missing full stops in this short story. Put in the full stops so that the story makes sense. *(1 mark for each correct answer)*

Amy was reading in her bedroom Her mum came in and asked her if she wanted to go to the fair Amy was so excited Later that afternoon Amy and her mum set off When they got there Amy saw the dodgems Amy wanted to have a go Her mum agreed and she had two rides Then Amy saw the ghost train Amy was a bit scared but she had a ride It was lots of fun

Unit 4 Using full stops

🔑 Key idea

A full stop marks the end of a sentence. It shows the reader where one idea ends.

Amy wanted a new book. She went to the shops to buy one.
Two full stops are used, as there are two ideas, each in their own sentence.

Spot the stop!

Look at these sentences. The full stop is in the wrong place. Cross it out and put it in the right place. *(1 mark for each correct answer)*

1 Adam. went to the shops
2 Amy saw. her sister
3 The man walked. into town
4 Tariq played with his friend. Sam
5 The lady had two. bags of shopping
6 Adam helped in the. garden
7 The. cow was in the field.
8 Amy flew her. kite on Saturday
9 John saw the. fireworks
10 The lady sang a beautiful. song

Unit 3 Sentence construction 3

Key idea

Sentences have a subject and an object.
Sentences must be clear and make sense.
The subject tells us 'who' or 'what' the sentence is about. The subject goes with the verb. The object of a sentence is the person or thing the subject is doing something to.

Who's doing what?

The subject of these sentences is missing.
Write in the subject for each one. Use the words in the box to help you. *(3 marks for each correct answer)*

1 The _____ sat in his kennel.
2 The _____ played with her kittens.
3 The _____ read a story in Assembly.
4 The _____ ate a carrot.
5 A _____ flew onto the tree.

| dog teacher |
| rabbit |
| cat bird |

Finish the sentence

The object in each of these sentences is missing. Write in the object for each one. Use the words in the box to help you.

(3 marks for each correct answer)

1 The boy batted the _____.
2 The postman dropped a _____.
3 The dog found a long, white _____.
4 The cow chewed the _____.
5 The bird sat on the _____.

| letter bone |
| ball grass |
| branch |

5

Sentence construction 2

🔑 Key idea

A sentence is a group of words which carries a meaning.
Sentences must make sense.

    Amy walked to school.

This sentence tells us how Amy got to school. It makes sense and is a complete idea.

Correct it!

These sentences have got mixed up. Underline the wrong word and write the correct one at the end of the sentence. *(3 marks for each correct answer)*

1 The cat was barking. _____   4 The dog drank the milk. _____

2 The bear was very tiny. _____   5 A rabbit lives in a swamp. _____

3 An ant is big and furry. _____   6 A crocodile lives in a hutch. _____

Get it right!

These sentences do not make sense. Change the word in bold so that the sentence makes sense. *(2 marks for each correct answer)*

1 Amy **are** a very nice girl. _____

2 Tariq **have** a cat. _____

3 The dogs **has** long tails. _____

4 Dad **like** ice cream. _____

5 The **shoe** were too tight. _____

6 I think Adam **are** a very kind boy. _____

Finish the sentence

Choose a verb to complete each sentence.

(1 mark for each correct answer)

> swam   drove   ran
> danced   watched
> barked   washed
> played   drilled   changed

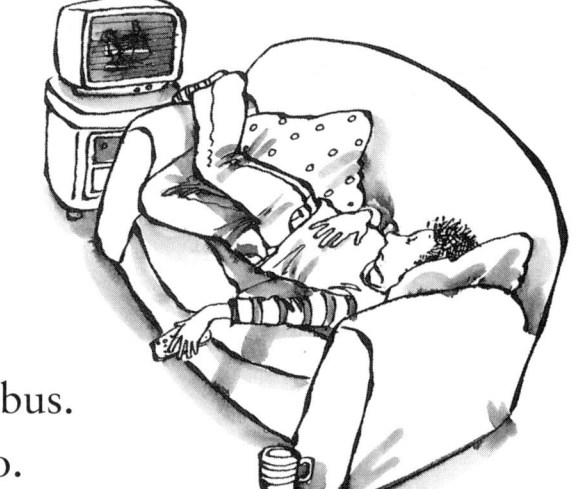

1 The lady _____ for the bus.
2 Tariq _____ at the disco.
3 Tariq _____ T.V. after school.
4 The dog _____ at the old man.
5 Tariq _____ his hands.
6 The magician _____ a bird into a rabbit!
7 The dentist _____ Tariq's tooth.
8 Tariq and Adam _____ football in the park.
9 Adam _____ in the pool.
10 Tariq's dad _____ to school in his new car.

Spot the verb!

Some of these sentences have a verb missing! Try to spot them, putting a tick or a cross after each sentence. Tick if the verb is there or put a cross if the verb is missing. *(1 mark for each correct answer)*

1 Tariq shut the door.
2 Mary the car.
3 Amy the park.
4 I saw a bird.
5 The boy seven.
6 Jill watched the film.
7 Tariq cut the string.
8 He the new cards.
9 The cup is red.
10 Tariq read two books.

Sentence construction 1

🔑 Key idea

A verb is a "doing" or a "being" word. All sentences need a verb to say what is happening.

Who's doing what?

Look at each of these pictures and write the verb which shows what the person is doing in each one. Choose the verbs from the box. *(1 mark for each correct answer)*

| singing | running | fishing | swimming | drinking |
| cooking | crying | writing | eating | kicking |

Grammar Starter Level Workbook

Contents

Unit 1	Sentence construction 1	page 2
Unit 2	Sentence construction 2	page 4
Unit 3	Sentence construction 3	page 5
Unit 4	Using full stops	page 6
Unit 5	Capital letters	page 8
Unit 6	Word order in sentences	page 10
Unit 7	Uses of capital letters	page 12
Unit 8	Linking words	page 14
Unit 9	Organisational devices	page 15
Unit 10	Question marks	page 16
Unit 12	Exclamation marks	page 18
Unit 13	Commas	page 19
Unit 14	Speech marks	page 20
Unit 15	Speech bubbles	page 22
Unit 16	Ways of presenting text	page 23
Unit 18	Commas in lists	page 24
Unit 19	Regular past tense	page 26
Unit 20	Tricky past tenses!	page 28
Unit 21	Does my sentence make sense?	page 30
Unit 22	Question words	page 32

Author: Chris Wardle

Ginn
Halley Court, Jordan Hill, Oxford OX2 8EJ
a division of Harcourt Education Limited

www.myprimary.co.uk
Help and support for teachers plus the widest range of education solutions

Ginn is a registered trademark of Harcourt Education Limited

© Harcourt Education Limited 2005

This book is copyright and reproduction of the whole or part without the publishers' written permission is prohibited.

Key Grammar Workbook Starter Level
ISBN: 978 0602 20679 6
Starter Level Easy Order Pack: 978 0602 20621 5
Starter Level Workbook 6 Pack: 978 0602 20643 7

First published 2005

20 19 18 17 16
15 14

Cover illustration by Pet Gotohda
Cover design by Tom Cole
Designed by Nicki Wise, Te Marama Design
Illustrations by Andrea Pretrlik Huseinovic, Maddy McClellan, Christina Bretschneider

Printed and bound by Malaysia (CTP-VVP)